FM
From Antenna
to
Audio

by
Leonard Feldman

HOWARD W. SAMS & CO., INC.
THE BOBBS-MERRILL CO., INC.
INDIANAPOLIS · KANSAS CITY · NEW YORK

FIRST EDITION

FIRST PRINTING—1969

Preface

On January 24, 1933, the late Major Edwin H. Armstrong applied to the United States Patent Office for a patent to cover a system of broadcasting which he titled simply, "Radiosignaling." The resulting patent—#1,941,069—was issued December 26 of that same year. (At that time, technology in the electronic field had not reached the level of complexity that required the patent office to spend approximately five years before issuing a patent.)

The patent called "Radiosignaling" was, in fact, the beginning of "wideband" fm broadcasting as we know it today. Actually, fm broadcasting principles were known long before 1933, but it took Armstrong to separate the techniques from those so long employed in a-m broadcasting, so that fm might realize its inherent advantages of low-interference, high-fidelity performance. Today, some thirty-six years later, nearly thirty million fm receivers are in use in the United States alone. Of these, some ten million are capable of reproducing "stereo fm" via the multiplexing techniques also conceived by Major Armstrong and refined primarily by another important inventor in the fm field, Murray G. Crosby.

Another encouraging factor in the belated popularity of fm was the recent decision of the Federal Communications Commission, with regard to separate programming for fm and a-m. This ruling decrees that owners of both a-m and fm stations must provide different program material for their a-m and fm outlets at least fifty percent of the time they are "on the air." In this way, the FCC elevated the status of fm from that of a tag-along "step-brother" to that of a full member of the broadcasting family.

In the chapters which follow, we have attempted to cover the subject of fm radio in the very broadest sense—from underlying propagation principles all the way through fm receivers, including the rudiments of fm receiver measurement and alignment. While we do not expect that the reader of this book will be enabled to design a new and better fm set, we do hope that he will have a clearer understanding of just what fm is all about—what makes it work—and what it is that makes it the ideal medium for high fidelity broadcasting.

I am deeply indebted to *Audio Magazine* and its publishers, North American Publishing Company, for permission to use much of the material which I originally wrote, in serialized form, for the publication. To Arthur Salsberg, Editor of *Audio*, for his assistance and encouragement, this book is fondly dedicated.

LEONARD FELDMAN

Contents

Chapter 1

A-M Versus FM Broadcasting

An unmodulated radio frequency carrier wave (with no intelligence or audio information imparted to it) has the same form whether it is radiated from the antenna of an fm transmitter or an a-m transmitter. Such a carrier wave may be represented as shown in Fig. 1-1. Unless we are told the frequency or number of alternations of the wave per second, there is no way to determine the type of transmitter which produced it—a-m or fm. In the United States, a-m broadcasting is confined to frequencies between 535 kHz (535,000 sinusoidal alternations per second) through 1605 kHz (1,605,000 alternations per second. This rather narrow spectrum refers to public broadcasting only. Other services such as police radio, marine telephone, amateur radio etc., are also assigned frequencies below and above the broadcast band.

The band of frequencies allocated to public fm broadcasting —from 88MHz to 108 MHz—is located between TV-Channel 6 and TV-Channel 7. Thus, if the waveform of an unmodulated fm transmitter could be observed on an oscilloscope, it would look just about like the representation in Fig. 1-1, except that many, many more alternations would appear in the same time span due to the much higher frequency of transmission.

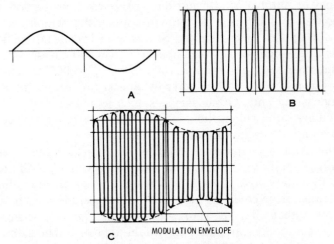

Fig. 1-1. Representation of unmodulated carrier wave.

AMPLITUDE MODULATION

For a complete understanding of how fm is so effective in reducing interference, we might well begin by considering the effects on a carrier wave when it is subjected to amplitude modulation and frequency modulation. In Fig. 1-2, the "A" diagram represents a low-frequency (audio) voltage, while the "B" diagram represents the unmodulated rf carrier. An amplitude-modulated carrier, shown in Fig. 1-2C, can be obtained with proper circuitry. The variations now present represent the audio intelligence. That is, the variations of rf amplitude trace out the pattern of the original audio information. An imaginary line (shown dotted) encompassing this tracing is often referred to as the "modulation envelope."

In amplitude modulation, there are physical limits imposed upon the amount of modulation possible. Fig. 1-3 clearly illustrates this. In Fig. 1-3A, we see a degree of modulation which causes the overall amplitude of the rf carrier to vary plus and minus 50 percent of its original amplitude. Fig. 1-3B illustrates an example of 100 percent amplitude modulation. Here, ampli-

A

B

MODULATION ENVELOPE

C

Fig. 1-2. Development of an amplitude-modulated rf carrier.

tude of the rf carrier varies plus and minus 100 percent of its original value. Note that on the "minus" portion of the cycle the carrier amplitude instantaneously reaches zero. If this degree of modulation is exceeded (Fig. 1-3), the entire carrier is "cut-off" for a significant portion of each audio cycle. Such a cut-off condition must result in distortion at the receiver, for the "modulation envelope" is no longer an exact replica of the original modulating (audio) information. Therefore, it cannot be accurately reproduced by the "demodulator" or detector in the a-m receiver.

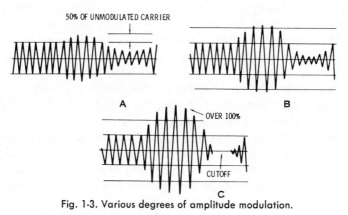

Fig. 1-3. Various degrees of amplitude modulation.

SIDEBANDS

Before analyzing frequency modulation, one more important factor about amplitude modulation must be understood. The process of amplitude modulation creates frequencies other than that of the fundamental carrier. For example, if a 1000 kHz carrier were to be modulated by an audio tone of 2000 Hz, we would find (either by mathematical analysis or by direct observation) that the resultant waveform contains the 1000 kHz carrier *plus* frequencies of 1002 kHz and 998 kHz. These new frequencies are called *sidebands*. The extra power used in modulating an rf carrier in amplitude goes into the sidebands. The basic rf carrier is left untouched.

As was pointed out earlier, the a-m broadcast band is rather limited in spectrum. As a result of the inherent generation of a pair of sidebands above and below the carrier, the Federal Communications Commission (FCC) had to set limits on the highest audio frequency that might be used to modulate an rf carrier in the a-m field. This limit generally is 5 kHz for most a-m stations. Thus, when a 5 kHz audio note is transmitted, a total of 10 kHz (5 kHz above and 5 kHz below the center rf frequency) must be reserved for a given station if the sidebands of one station are not to "spill over" into the next. This sets a theoretical limitation on the number of stations possible on the dial in a given locality to a maximum of 107. (1605 − 535 = 1070 kHz. 1070 kHz/10 kHz = 107.)

In actual practice, the FCC would not allocate station frequencies 10 kHz apart in one locality because most commercially made receivers would not be sufficiently selective to "tune out" the adjacent station. Thus, 20 kHz separation is the usual practice. This limits the number of stations in an area to about 50.

In fm, the amplitude of the rf carrier remains constant at all times. It's the *frequency* of the carrier that is varied by modulation, as shown in Fig. 1-4. Again, a low-frequency audio tone is used to modulate the carrier. As the audio tone goes positive, the frequency of the fm carrier *increases* (more alternations per second), whereas, when the audio tone crosses the zero axis (and has no amplitude, instantaneously), the frequency of

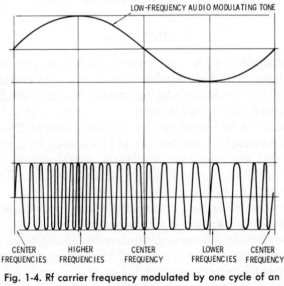

Fig. 1-4. Rf carrier frequency modulated by one cycle of an audio signal.

the carrier returns to its center or nominal value. Finally, when the audio modulating voltage goes negative, the carrier frequency *decreases* (fewer alternations per second).

The amount of carrier frequency variation about its nominal center is governed by the *amplitude* of the modulating voltage. To put it another way, a symphony orchestra playing loud passages will cause the carrier frequency to shift about its nominal center *more* than would a whispering vocalist. The frequency of the audio modulating voltage merely determines the rapidity with which the fm carrier swings above and below its center frequency.

To summarize, a *strong* audio signal (loud) will shift the carrier frequency about its nominal value to a greater extent than will a weak (soft) tone. The number of times per second that this frequency shift occurs is governed by the frequency or pitch of the modulating tone.

From the foregoing, you can see that the term "100 percent modulation" really has no specific meaning, in a physical sense or limitation, when applied to fm. However, because of certain other considerations that will be discussed shortly, maximum allowable "deviation" (amount of departure from "center frequency") has been set by the FCC as 75 kHz above and below the carrier frequency.

To minimize any possible interaction between stations, an additional 25 kHz is allotted on either side of these extremes. Therefore, each station is assigned a "bandwidth" of 200 kHz (75 kHz + 25 kHz about the center frequency). As a practical matter, the maximum number of stations that might be assigned in a given locale would be (108 MHz − 88 MHz = 20 MHz = 20,000 kHz; 20,000/200 = 100). Again, in actual practice, the FCC seldom assigns stations closer than 400 kHz apart in an immediate geographical area.

FM SIDEBANDS

As was true in a-m, sidebands are formed as a carrier begins to be frequency modulated. So long as the frequency deviation is held to some minimum amount, only two sidebands are developed, just as in a-m.

The upper sideband will be removed in frequency by the frequency of the modulating tone above the carrier and the lower sideband will be displaced below the center frequency by the same amount. So far, the situation is the same as in a-m. However, as we increase the amplitude of the modulating tone (and therefore the frequency deviation of the carrier) beyond a minimum value, additional significant sidebands appear at multiples above and below the carrier. Thus, if a strong audio signal of 1000 Hz is used to modulate a carrier centered at 90 MHz, sidebands will appear at 90.001 MHz, 90.002 MHz, 90.003 MHz, etc., and 89.999 MHz, 89.998 MHz, 89.997 MHz, and so on.

Note that we used the term *significant* sidebands. In theory, an *infinite* number of sidebands are produced but, at any given modulating intensity, only a finite number of these have sufficient power to be of any significance.

We have seen that whenever sidebands are formed, they are spaced apart by a frequency equal to the modulating tone frequency. This may be seen in Fig. 1-5, in which the modulating frequency is 1 kHz and modulation intensity is strong enough to produce seven significant sidebands above and below the center carrier frequency.

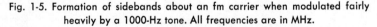

(A) *Unmodulated carrier at 90.0 MHz.*

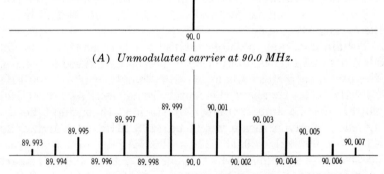

(B) *Approximate amplitude of sidebands of frequency-modulated carrier.*

Fig. 1-5. Formation of sidebands about an fm carrier when modulated fairly heavily by a 1000-Hz tone. All frequencies are in MHz.

Now, suppose we wish to transmit a 15 kHz tone instead of 1 kHz and that the intensity of modulation is to be the same. Fig. 1-6 indicates that seven sidebands still result above and below the carrier, but since the modulating frequency is now 15 kHz instead of 1 kHz, the seventh sideband is fully 105 kHz above and below the carrier frequency.

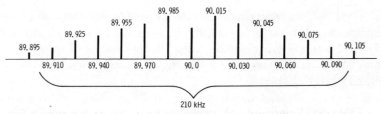

Fig. 1-6. Side bands on an fm carrier when it is modulated by a 15 kHz tone.

We therefore observe that the frequency bandwidth required by a frequency-modulated carrier depends upon two factors: *intensity* of the applied modulating audio voltage and *frequency* of this voltage. From these considerations the term *modulation index* evolves, which is defined as the ratio of fm carrier deviation to the audio frequency causing the deviation. In current U. S. practice, the maximum deviation permitted is 75 kHz and the highest audio frequency used is 15 kHz (hence, the "high-fidelity" connotations for fm, as opposed to the 5 kHz limit generally imposed with a-m). Thus, the modulation index for these conditions is 75 kHz/15 kHz or 5.

Complex calculations show, however, that a modulation index of 5 always produces no less than 8 significant sidebands above and below the main carrier frequency. It is always somewhat confusing to the student of fm to learn that, although the carrier frequency is never actually shifted by more than ±75 kHz above and below the center, *sidebands* do appear beyond these limits. For example, if a 15,000 Hz tone were to fully modulate an fm carrier (index 5) out to ±75 kHz, we have said that 8 sidebands would be formed on either side of the carrier. The most remote of these sidebands would be 8 × 15 kHz removed from center frequency, or 120 kHz above and below the carrier center.

In actual practice, a 15 kHz note will seldom have enough intensity to deviate the transmitter to its 75 kHz limits, though in theory this condition is possible and would be within the limits set by the FCC. The FCC rules merely state that the maximum *shift* of the carrier frequency must never exceed 75 kHz. Often, when the 75 kHz shift is fully utilized, significant sidebands appear outside the 75 kHz limits. Usually, their energy contribution is quite small and, besides, the extra guard band of that additional 25 kHz helps to reduce the possibility of interstation interference.

Thus far, we have examined the nature of fm and a-m modulation in relation to imparting information to an rf carrier. Table 1-1 is a comparison between the two forms of modulation and summarizes some of the significant facts which will help to clarify later chapters.

Table 1-1. Comparison of Amplitude and Frequency Modulation

	A-M	FM
Public Frequencies	535-1605 kHz	88-108 MHz
Carrier Amplitude	Varies from 0 to 200% of nominal	Constant
Carrier Frequency	Constant	Varies ±75 kHz from center
Audio Loudness Varies	Amplitude of carrier	Frequency of carrier
Audio Frequency Varies	Rapidity of carrier amplitude changes	Rapidity of carrier frequency changes
Sidebands Produced (Significant)	Two—upper and lower	2 to 16, depending upon modulation intensity
Highest Frequency (Audio)	5,000 Hz (with some exceptions)	15,000 Hz
Station Bandwidth	10 kHz (some exceptions)	200 kHz (including 25 kHz guard band at each extreme)

Chapter 2

Noise and
Interference in FM

CO-CHANNEL INTERFERENCE

If we examine the difference between the propagation of fm and a-m broadcast signals, we see two outstanding advantages of wideband fm (as presently broadcast): outstanding fidelity and reduced interference. The term "interference" applies to more than merely "static." It covers any voltage arriving at the input of a receiver or created within the circuitry of the receiver itself which interferes with satisfactory reception of the desired station signal.

For a better understanding of fm, we shall next examine the significant forms of interference prevalent in radio broadcasting and show why these forms of interference are less dominant in fm reception than in a-m reception.

A frequent annoyance in a-m listening (particularly at night, when reception range increases) is the piercing whistle heard when two stations are operating within the same channel. This whistle is produced whenever the frequency difference between the stations is equal to an audible frequency. In the case of adjacent channels (10 kHz apart), the whistle is often eliminated in quality a-m receivers by the incorporation of a 10 kHz "whistle filter." This circuit effectively suppresses all frequencies around 10 kHz without significantly attenuating desired frequencies (5 kHz and below, for a-m).

In this instance, however, we are discussing co-channel interference, where two stations (however distant from each other geographically) are occupying the same assigned channel but, because of permitted tolerances, may have carrier frequencies several hundred cycles apart. Since the two carriers are so close in frequency, both signals pass through the circuitry of the a-m receiver until, at the second detector, the beat note appears. In typical a-m situations, the interfering signal will be noticed when it is only ¹⁄₁₀₀ as strong as the desired signal. Contrast this with the situation in fm, where the desired signal need be only twice as strong as the interfering signal to *completely* override it!

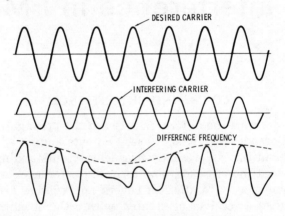

Fig. 2-1. Production of a beat frequency by addition of a desired carrier and an interfering carrier.

Fig. 2-1 represents two rf signals, differing slightly in frequency and considerably in amplitude. The resultant waveform (derived by algebraically adding the instantaneous amplitudes of each) is shown in the lower portion of the drawing. You will note that the resultant amplitude varies at a rate equal to the difference between the two frequencies from which it is derived. If the two frequencies differ by, say, 400 Hz, the amplitude of the resultant will increase and decrease 400 times per second. This a-m variation, applied to an a-m receiver, would, of course, be detected in the course of the normal functioning of this type of receiver, producing the familiar beat note previously mentioned.

While the effect observed in Fig. 2-1 may be correctly termed a form of "undesired amplitude modulation," a second, less obvious form of modulation takes place in such situations— phase modulation. That is, with respect to the larger (desired) of the two signals shown in Fig. 2-1, the added resultant waveform alternately leads and lags by some finite number of degrees. The degree of phase lag or lead depends upon the relative amplitudes of the desired and undesired rf signals.

For illustrative purposes, let us suppose that the undesired waveform is ½ as large as the desired signal. Under these circumstances, the phase shift (lag alternating with lead) will amount to 30 degrees. Now, phase modulation is really just another form of fm modulation. In fact, many forms of fm transmitter systems employ simple phase modulation as the first step in the creation of wide-band frequency modulation. So in the context of our analysis, the two terms may be thought of as being synonymous.

To summarize, whenever two signals (close in frequency) appear at the input of a receiver, their resultant will be amplitude and phase modulated.

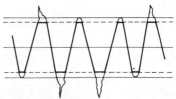

Fig. 2-2. Action of a limiter circuit in an fm receiver. Amplitude variations caused by interference are removed.

In a-m sets, the amplitude variation creates the "beat" or whistle note. The phase modulation adds a small amount of frequency modulation. Both of these new components constitute a departure from the original signal and, in an fm set, must be eliminated. Amplitude variation is by far the simpler to remove. This is done by means of "limiter" stages to which we shall devote considerable discussion in later chapters. For the moment, Fig. 2-2 will serve to illustrate the principles of limiting. Since an fm receiver need sense only changes of carrier frequency, we can, by use of proper circuitry, "slice off" any amplitude variations without removing any desired intelligence from the signal.

The undesired phase modulation is not so easily eliminated. However, we can quickly show that its effect on performance will be minimal, compared with the normal or desired frequency excursions caused by the program information.

Using the example cited earlier, it can be shown that if the desired and undesired signal differ in amplitude by a ratio of two to one and in frequency by 400 cycles, then the indirect fm produced by the resultant phase modulation will be ±200 Hz. That is, the resultant carrier will have an added frequency shift (over and above that caused by normal program material) of 200 Hz above and below the central or nominal frequency. If we compare this shift with the normal maximum deviation of 75,000 Hz authorized by the FCC for wideband fm we see that the maximum signal-to-interference ratio is 375 to 1, or better than 50 decibels. To put it another way, this little bit of undesired "fm" interference will be all but inaudible under these conditions. And, bear in mind, that these conditions, as stated, were quite extreme. It is not usual to have an interfering signal nearly half as great as the desired signal. More typical might be ratios of 1 to 10 or 1 to 20, in which case the effect of the undesired "fm" would be far less.

STRONG-SIGNAL DOMINATION

A series of vector diagrams, shown in Fig. 2-3, will help to clarify the concept of "capture," which is the selection of the stronger of two signals in fm. While the full specification of *capture ratio* (ability of a receiver to favor the stronger of two fm signals received on the same frequency) depends in part upon certain facets of the receiver design itself, the ability of fm in general to discriminate against the weaker of two incoming signals is inherent in the fm system, rather than in one given receiver design.

In all of the diagrams of Fig. 2-3, let us assume that vector 1 represents the desired carrier, rotating at 100 MHz. Vector 2, the undesired signal, is also rotating, but at a frequency of 100.005 MHz, 5000 Hz higher in frequency than the desired signal. (All rotations, by the way, are assumed to move counterclockwise.) Since vector 2 is rotating slightly faster than vector 1, it will, in effect, pull ahead of vector 1 as we look at the successive diagrams. The resultant vector, T, will

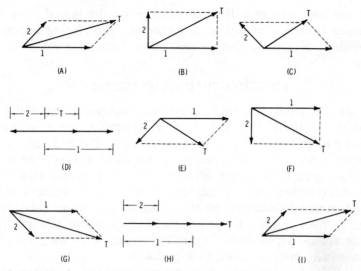

Fig. 2-3. Vectorial representation of resultant T when a smaller carrier (2) interferes with a larger carrier (1).

also rotate. If we "stop the action" at various points in the rotation of vector 2 relative to vector 1 and examine resultant T, we see that it fluctuates or "wobbles" about vector 1.

In Fig. 2-3C, it has shifted to its maximum position ahead of vector 1; whereas, at 2-3E it has fallen maximally behind vector 1. The back and forth fluctuations of the resultant vector T represent the phase modulation of the resultant carrier. Note, however, that the resultant is wobbling back and forth about vector 1, the larger signal. Thus, vector 1 (the desired signal) and the resultant vector T have the same *average* frequency. The signal heard in the speaker of the fm set will be determined primarily by vector 1. If we were to make signal 2 the larger of the pair, the resultant would swing about vector 2, and it would predominate.

Further examination discloses that the amplitude of resultant vector T differs from that of desired vector 1, but we have already stated that these amplitude variations are readily eliminated by means of limiters in the design of the given receiver. The phase modulations of the resultant, while still present, represent a minimal fm deviation, compared with the normal program deviation, and can therefore be ignored, to a large extent. Once the ratio of the interfering to the desired signal reaches 1 to 2, the effect of the smaller signal upon the larger becomes negligible, whether the interfering signal is another, distant station or any other form of random noise.

ADJACENT-CHANNEL INTERFERENCE

As we noted earlier, fm channel frequencies are 200 kHz apart, but the FCC usually assigns stations at least two channels apart (400 kHz) in any given locality. The fact that interference can still occur arises from two factors. First, the selectivity characteristic of a given receiver may permit this form of interference. Second, extreme sidebands caused by certain instantaneous modulations of two adjacent stations may interact to form audible frequencies at the output of the receiver. The region of possible sideband interaction between two adjacent channels is shown in Fig. 2-4.

Recall, for example, that with a modulation index of 5 (normal practice), 8 significant sidebands can be produced and, if by some unusual circumstance, a musical note at 15 kHz were of sufficient amplitude to cause a modulation index of 5, the most extreme frequency away from center would be 8 × 15, or 120 kHz, well within the guard band of the next adjacent channel. If, at the same moment, the adjacent station were transmitting a 15-kHz musical component causing a mod-

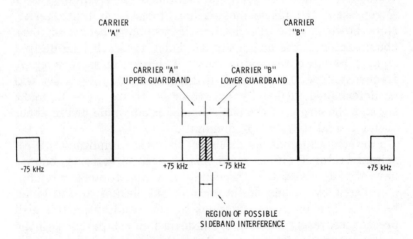

Fig. 2-4. Interaction between adjacent channel signals on the fm band. Interference is minimized by assigning channels 400 kHz apart in any one geographical area.

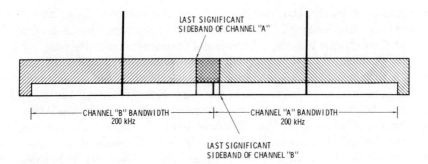

LAST SIGNIFICANT
SIDEBAND OF CHANNEL "A"

|←—————— CHANNEL "B" BANDWIDTH ——————→|←——— CHANNEL "A" BANDWIDTH ———→|
200 kHz   200 kHz

LAST SIGNIFICANT
SIDEBAND OF CHANNEL "B"

Fig. 2-5. Under actual conditions described in text, fully 25 kHz of sideband interaction will take place between the two adjacent channels shown here.

ulation index of, say, 4 (resulting in seven significant sidebands), the extreme sideband frequency produced would be
15 kHz × 7 or 105 kHz. There would be 25 kHz of sideband
interaction possible under these conditions, as shown in Fig.
2-5.

The selectivity characteristics of a given receiver also play
an important part in this adjacent channel form of interference. Ideally, the perfect response characteristic for the
combined rf and i-f portions of an fm receiver would be that
represented in Fig. 2-6. If this response could be achieved in
practice, adjacent channel problems would not exist. Interest-
ingly, some very late models perfected in the last year or so by
one or two manufacturers actually come close to this type of
response curve. Crystal filters combined with integrated circuits, as well as multisection, carefully calculated bandpass
filters (as opposed to the usual tuned-primary, tuned-secondary
"i-f transformers"), are finally beginning to come upon the fm
tuner scene.

More often than not, however, a typical response curve of the
tuned circuits of an fm receiver would be that shown in Fig.
2-7. Note that there is still significant response to signals well
beyond the 200-kHz channel bandwidth assigned to any given

Fig. 2-6. Idealized response curve of
tunable portion of an fm receiver.

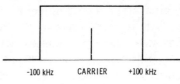

-100 kHz   CARRIER   +100 kHz

station. Clearly, the bandwidth of such a receiver does extend beyond the ideal ±100 kHz, however attenuated the response at the extreme may be. With such a response, it is quite possible to receive sidebands emanating from adjacent channel stations.

As a practical matter, the situation is still much better in this regard for fm than it is for a-m. For one thing, the FCC has been careful in its assignment of station carrier frequencies. The use of 25 kHz guard bands further decreases the possibility of adjacent bands interfering with each other. Also, the higher frequencies used in fm are limited essentially to line-of-sight transmission as opposed to the lower a-m frequencies where long distance reception often occurs, particularly at night. Finally, the inherent characteristic of fm, wherein all that is required is a two-to-one signal advantage for practical elimination of interference, renders this form of reception far less susceptible to interference as compared with a-m, where dominance of a strong signal does not really occur until the stronger signal is at least 100 times more powerful than the weaker one.

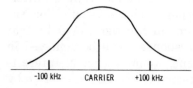

Fig. 2-7. Practical response curve achieved by most commercial receivers.

STATIC INTERFERENCE

The last form of interference which we shall consider for the present is "static"—a form of interference so familiar to the a-m listener, especially during a summer thunderstorm. Studies have shown that while static contains many, many bands of frequencies, the greatest concentration of electrical energy is in the lower frequency region. Thus, with fm we not only have the advantage of the "dominance of the stronger signal" effect (not to mention the use of amplitude limiters which strip away much of the static interference), but the additional advantage of the high-frequency bands allocated for fm use. Finally, more distant thunderstorms, etc., seldom cause any interference because they are beyond the "line-of-sight" limitations of fm reception. All of these factors work in the right direction to make fm the noise-free, static-free, interference-free listening medium that it has proved to be. Do not conclude that fm receivers are *entirely* noise free. We shall now examine noise in fm to the degree that it *does* exist and consider what is done to eliminate it or reduce it to an irreducible minimum.

Even in the complete absence of "external" noise sources, there is a practical limit to the weakest signal that can be received by an fm tuner or receiver. This limit, usually set by the first rf (radio frequency) stages of the set, is determined by two main sources of noise: *thermal agitation*, and internally generated *tube* or *transistor noise*.

THERMAL NOISE

Thermal agitation arises from the random motion of electrons in any conductor having a finite resistance or impedance. The amount of voltage developed by thermal agitation in a source impedance at room temperature (27-deg. C.) can be simplified from a lengthier equation to:

$$V = \sqrt{1.6 \times 10^{-20} BR_s}$$

where,
  B is the bandwidth involved (200 kHz per channel for fm),
  R_s is the source impedance at the antenna input terminals (usually 300 ohms but sometimes 75 ohms).

By solving this equation, we find that the thermal voltage at the input to a receiver is about 0.98 microvolts for a 300-ohm input circuit and about 0.49 microvolts for a 75-ohm input circuit. Note that the wider the bandwidth, the larger the amount of thermal-noise voltage developed. As far as this one point is concerned, narrow-band fm produces less intrinsic noise than wideband fm, all other factors being equal. As observed previously, however, all other factors are not equal, and the advantages of wideband fm far outweigh this minimal noise consideration.

TUBE AND TRANSISTOR NOISE

In the case of tube rf amplifiers, current flow from cathode to plate is not uniform and continuous, but rather a movement of separate particles—the electrons. Instantaneous fluctuations of the number of electrons flowing (even when "steady-state" current is flowing) represent a noise component. In transistors, too, excess noise is produced by thermal noise in the external lead resistances and by "shot noise" from charge carriers entering and leaving the base element of the transistor. In both cases, the energy of the noise is distributed throughout the frequency spectrum and therefore resembles noise arising from the more easily calculated thermal agitation. For our purposes, therefore, we can combine both forms of noise under the general heading of *random noise*.

Random noise includes many frequencies. When no carrier is present, the various frequencies present beat with each other to produce the loud hiss normally associated with the act of tuning between stations. This is true of both a-m and fm receivers. In the case of fm sets, interstation noise is actually greater because of the wide bandwidth designed into the circuitry. To eliminate interstation noise, many manufacturers incorporate "muting" circuits which, in one way or another, block the audio output stages in the absence of a station carrier signal.

When a station is received, interactions occur between the station carrier and each of the random voltages. Two effects are thus produced: amplitude modulation of the carrier, and phase modulation which indirectly results in frequency modulation. In the presence of a sufficiently strong station, amplitude modulation will be removed by the built-in limiters. As for the fm produced, it will depend upon the separation in frequency between the noise voltage and the carrier, increasing in amount with this separation in frequency.

The graph in Fig. 2-8 illustrates this principle and, while it does not purport to show actual amplitudes, it does illustrate the fact that the noise interference becomes greater as the frequency between the carrier and the noise voltages increases. While the end of the diagram extends to 75 kHz, our hearing extends, for all practical purposes, to only 15 kHz. Thus, we can disregard the noise content above 15 kHz.

In Fig. 2-9 all the audible noise associated with a-m transmission (assuming that the receiver was able to respond up to 15 kHz) has been superimposed upon the "noise triangle" of Fig. 2-8. Since total noise represents the *area* encompassed by

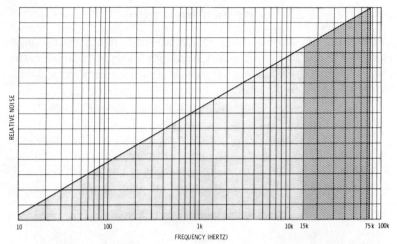

Fig. 2-8. Noise in an fm set increases with frequency between carrier and interfering signal. Shaded area is audible fm noise.

each plot, it is evident that the fm gives less noise in the output. Mathematically, the difference can be shown to be a ratio of 8.65 to 1, or approximately 19 dB. In other words, because of the intrinsic characteristics of fm, it is more effective in reducing noise than the a-m methods of transmission, providing, of course, that a carrier is present.

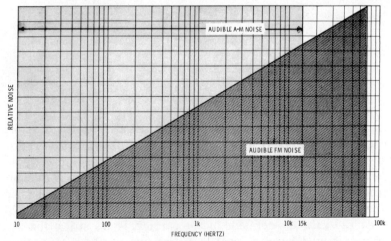

Fig. 2-9. Comparison of noise audible in fm and a-m. Triangular portion represents fm noise; entire rectangle (to 15 kHz) represents a-m noise.

NOISE AND DEVIATION

Deviation (extent of modulation above and below the main carrier frequency) has a direct bearing on signal-to-noise ratio. As was mentioned earlier, present fm practice employs a deviation ratio of 5 to 1. That is, a maximum carrier shift of ±75 kHz is permitted and the highest audio frequency transmitted is 15 kHz ($75/15 = 5$).

If we were to limit the maximum deviation, the signal-to-noise improvement over a-m would diminish correspondingly, as illustrated in Fig. 2-10. Note that even if the deviation maximum were reduced to 15 kHz (a deviation ratio of 1 to 1), we

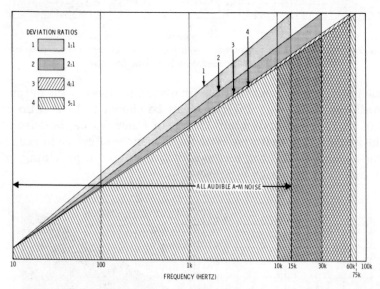

Fig. 2-10. Signal-to-noise ratio degrades as deviation ratio decreases.

would still obtain a better signal-to-noise ratio than is possible with a-m. Conversely, if we were able to utilize deviation ratios in excess of 5 to 1, the improvement in signal-to-noise would continue, but then we would run into spectrum assignment troubles. For example, if we attempted to use a deviation ratio of 8, with a maximum audio frequency of 15 kHz, we would need 120 kHz on each side of the carrier. If we still utilized a 25-kHz guard band at each extreme, we would have a total bandwidth of 290 kHz instead of the present 200 kHz. This

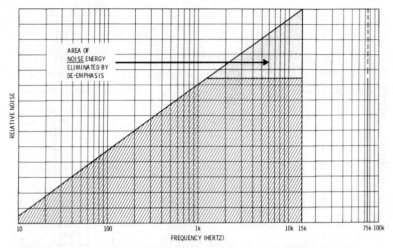

Fig. 2-11. Noise reduction brought about by de-emphasis. Compare shaded area with that of Fig. 2-9.

would effectively reduce the number of possible stations in any given geographical location.

PRE-EMPHASIS AND DE-EMPHASIS

In studies of the frequency and energy content of music and speech, it was determined long ago that most of the energy is contained in the low and middle frequencies. In addition, it is well known that the noise which irritates listeners most is that found at the higher audio frequencies, above 4 or 5 kHz or so.

These two facts clear the way for use of pre-emphasis and de-emphasis. Pre-emphasis involves boosting the relative level of high frequencies during the process of transmission in accordance with the curve shown in Fig. 2-12. Bear in mind that this curve represents the response of some audio amplifier ahead of the modulating stage of the transmitter. It does not mean that the high frequencies will overmodulate the transmitter because, remember, the high-frequency energy content of music and speech is generally so much lower than the low and middle tones that, left unaccentuated, they would never even come close to effecting a 75 kHz deviation of the main carrier.

A typical circuit for accomplishing the correct amount of pre-emphasis accompanies the response curve of Fig. 2-12.

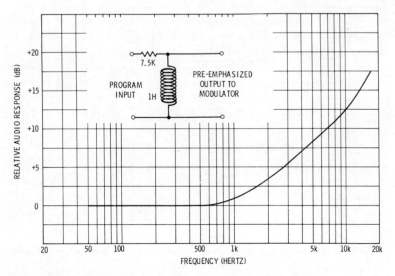

Fig. 2-12. Standard fm pre-emphasis, as practiced by fm broadcasters in the U.S.

Now, perhaps, you can understand why an fm tuner response curve is anything but "flat," but rather follows the curve shown in Fig. 2-13.

By *de*-emphasizing the high frequencies in the receiver, the overall frequency response of the system (including trans-

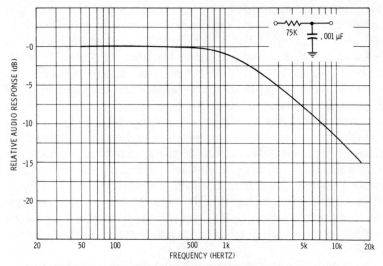

Fig. 2-13. Standard 75-μs de-emphasis built into fm tuners to restore "flat" response.

mitter and receiver) is restored to the desired "flat" or uniform characteristic which is a prerequisite to all high fidelity equipment. More important, however, is that by including de-emphasis, the objectionable high-frequency noise is considerably reduced, compared to what it would have been had we not bothered.

The "triangular" response originally illustrated in Fig. 2-8 is effectively changed to that of Fig. 2-11 wherein a large portion of the noise has been "sliced off." The circuit generally used to accomplish de-emphasis is shown in Fig. 2-13. Note that it consists only of a resistor and a capacitor, chosen so that the product of R and C equals 75×10^{-6}. This product, referred to as a time constant, is expressed as 75 microseconds.

Chapter 3

Signal Propagation and Receiving Antennas

FM BROADCASTING

Having examined the noise-free, high fidelity characteristics of fm transmission, we shall now devote some time to a study of how an fm signal is electronically created and how it is radiated for ultimate reception by an fm receiver.

There are two general methods used for the generation of an fm signal. The first is sometimes called "direct fm." This involves varying the frequency of the main oscillator of the transmitter in accordance with the modulation to be impressed. In the second method, frequency modulation is achieved by varying the *phase* of a signal obtained from a stable, crystal oscillator.

Direct FM

The most obvious and direct way to obtain a frequency-modulated wave is through variation of one of the frequency-determining elements of an ordinary, high-frequency oscillator. A crude method of doing this is illustrated in Fig. 3-1. Here, a "condenser" microphone is connected in parallel with the frequency-determining L and C of a familiar Hartley oscillator.

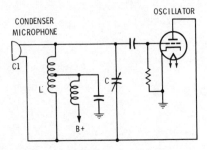

Fig. 3-1. Simple frequency modulator using variable capacitance in oscillator "tank" circuit (L, C, and C1).

As long as no sound is fed to the microphone, the resonant frequency will be determined by the sum of the capacitances of the microphone and C in parallel with the coil, L. This frequency represents the resting, or carrier frequency, translated to fm terminology. As sound waves hit the microphone capacitor plate, it vibrates closer to, and further away from the fixed plate. Thus, its capacitance (and hence the total capacitance in the circuit) is altered. The instantaneous frequency is therefore caused to shift above and below the central resting frequency, and a frequency-modulated signal is developed.

In actual practice, a reactance tube (or transistor) acts as a variable inductance (L) or capacitance (C) across a predetermined resonant circuit, as shown in Fig. 3-2. Audio information applied to the grid of V1 effectively changes the apparent "L" of the output circuit which, in turn, varies the oscillator

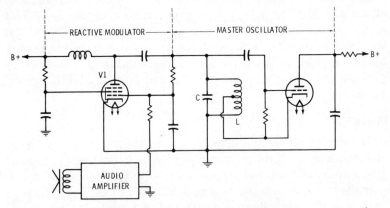

Fig. 3-2. Reactance tube used as a variable capacitive reactance across the master oscillator tank circuit (L, C).

frequency. In practice, the oscillator frequency is kept at around 5 MHz, and the reactance modulator is able to shift that frequency by only about ± 5 kHz. Frequency multipliers, such as doublers and triplers, are then used to boost the center frequency up to the 88-108 MHz band required for fm broadcasting. In so doing, the modulation swing is correspondingly increased. As an example, if the 5-MHz basic oscillator frequency is multiplied by 18 (say, by doubling once, and tripling twice), the resulting frequency will be 90 MHz. Since the modulation (or change of frequency) undergoes the same multiplying factor, a total modulation of 4 kHz × 18, or 72 kHz, will result; just about right for the usual maximum of ±75 kHz required in standard fm broadcasting. A block diagram of a transmitter using the reactance tube approach is shown in Fig. 3-3.

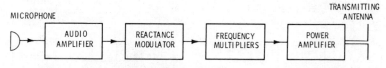

Fig. 3-3. Block diagram of fm transmitter using "direct" fm approach.

Since the basic oscillator used in reactance modulation transmitters is not crystal controlled (a crystal-controlled oscillator could not be "forced" to shift frequency, since the crystal determines the resonant point), if no further steps were taken to stabilize the transmitter, its frequency might be expected to drift considerably. The FCC requires that center frequency be maintained within ±2 kHz. In the example cited, this would represent a stability of approximately ±111 Hz at the 5-MHz master oscillator level. To ensure such extreme stability, a crystal oscillator is used as a reference to produce a correcting voltage (very much like the familiar afc voltage used in receivers to help keep stations tuned in), as shown in Fig. 3-4.

Phase Modulation

When a carrier wave shifts back and forth in phase while maintaining a constant frequency, this shifting causes the same effect as if the frequency itself were being instantaneously varied. This variation represents a moderate amount of frequency modulation and is the basis of all phase-modulation

33

schemes for producing an fm signal. The indirect fm produced will depend upon the maximum angle that the carrier wave is shifted, and on the frequency at which the shift takes place.

In one variation of the phase-modulation approach, the maximum practical phase angle that can be produced in the phase modulator is 30 degrees (approximately half a radian). Since the fm produced equals the product of modulating frequency and phase angle, for a 15-kHz modulating frequency, we could expect the resulting fm to be 15 kHz × 0.5 (radians), or ±7.5 kHz. Offhand, you might expect that, starting with a 10 MHz crystal-controlled oscillator (the chief advantage of all the phase modulation approaches is that a crystal-controlled oscillator can be used as the master oscillator), one would only have to multiply the frequency 10 times to come up with a 100-MHz carrier frequency and a ±75-kHz modulation capacity.

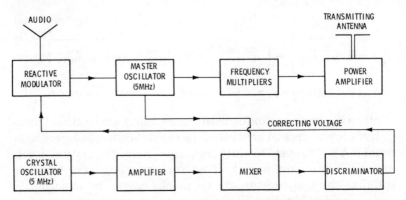

Fig. 3-4. Block diagram of fm transmitter having crystal-controlled reference.

Examination of the mathematical relationships just stated discloses that this would only be true for a 15-kHz modulating tone. At 50 Hz (the lower end of the audio spectrum desired in fm transmission) we would get fm amounting to only 50 Hz × 0.5 (radians) = 25 Hz! In phase modulation, therefore, something must be done so that regardless of modulating frequency, the net amount of fm will be the same, notwithstanding the audio modulating frequency. An RC corrective network, such as shown in Fig. 3-6, must be interposed between the audio source and the phase modulator, so that the higher frequencies will be attenuated relative to the lowest audio modulating frequency (in this case, 50 Hz). Therefore, *all* audio

34

frequencies concerned will produce only a minimal 25 Hz of indirect fm when the phase angle is 0.5 radian.

If we divide 75,000 Hz (the desired total deviation at carrier frequency) by 25 Hz, it becomes apparent that doublers and triplers would have to be arranged to multiply the starting frequency by some 3000 times. That is, if we wished to have a carrier frequency of 90 MHz, we would have to start with a crystal master oscillator having a frequency of 90,000,000/ 3000, or 30,000 Hz. While crystals of such low resonant frequency can be made, a more practical approach is to use a crystal having a frequency of around 200 kHz. After several doublers and triplers, we achieve a frequency of 32.4 MHz, as shown in Fig. 3-5. At this point, a second crystal oscillator output, at 27.4 MHz, is heterodyned with the 32.4-MHz signal to produce a 5-MHz output. This signal is then tripled and doubled in much the same way as was shown in Fig. 3-3, resulting in a final output of 90 MHz having a maximum deviation of ±72.9 kHz, as required.

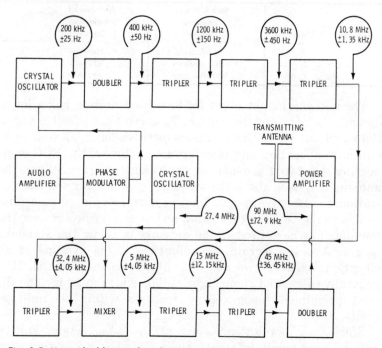

Fig. 3-5. Using doublers and triplers to produce a 90-MHz fm signal from a 200-kHz oscillator signal.

Several variations of phase modulation have been developed over the years, many of which are in current use in practical transmitter installations. One, known as the Armstrong system, simplifies the method used to obtain substantial phase modulation. Another, known as a Serrasoid Modulator, secures a relatively large amount of initial phase modulation, reducing the amount of frequency multiplication required to achieve a carrier frequency at the assigned fm frequency.

TRANSMITTER POWER & RANGE

The FCC has set up rules governing assignment of fm frequencies, maximum permitted radiated power, frequency separation between stations and allowable signal interference ratios. The various classes of station in service are shown in Table 3-1.

Table 3-1. Classes of FM Stations

Class	Max Effective Radiated Power	Antenna Ht Above Avg Terrain
A	3 kilowatts	300 feet
B	50 kilowatts	500 feet
C	100 kilowatts	2,000 feet

The antenna height of an fm broadcast station has a lot to do with the range of the station. To correct for possible variations and put all stations on a competitive basis, as well as to minimize allocation and interference problems, the FCC engineering standards provide for equivalent coverage. When the antenna height is above the standard specified for the class of station, the effective radiated power must be reduced according to a formula. On the other hand, no increase of power over the maximum is permitted if the antenna is below the standard height. Average terrain, by definition, is the average of all elevations between two and ten miles from the antenna. It is generally calculated along eight radials which must include the most prominent topographical features within the mileage limits.

Since very few antennas are at the same height, station powers have many different values. This has led to confusion on the part of both listeners and advertisers because some stations publicize their actual licensed rating, whereas others use the maximum ceiling value for that class of station. While these larger numbers may appear to make the station seem more powerful, the simple truth is that all fm stations operating with maximum facilities have equivalent coverage.

Channel Separation and Interference

While the FCC generally assigns frequencies at least 800 kHz apart in the same city, objectionable interference is not considered to exist when the channel separation is 400 kHz or greater. Therefore, fm stations in the same general area are often assigned to frequencies 400 kHz apart. Of course, the ability of the receiver to separate stations only 400 kHz apart is extremely important, and recalls earlier discussions in this book concerning adjacent channel interference, capture ratio, and associated measurement which describe this ability to discriminate between one station and the next.

The FCC considers the necessary signal strength for satisfactory service in city areas to be 1000 microvolts/meter. In rural areas, far removed from highways (and associated noise produced by automotive ignition), 50 microvolts/meter of signal strength is deemed adequate.

Signal *strength* in an area and signal *intensity* actually reaching your receiver may be two entirely different numbers unless you pay careful attention to antenna requirements.

FM RECEIVING ANTENNAS

There is, perhaps, no more misunderstood subject in all the world of fm than that of fm antennas. The fault lies both with users and manufacturers of fm receiving equipment. The former, accustomed to "built in" antennas as supplied on a-m equipment, have consistently resisted the need for an adequate antenna in fm applications. The latter, bowing to public pressure, have supplied all manner of makeshift "indoor" antennas, from a short length of wire to capacitive coupling to the power cord, to a T-shaped piece of 300-ohm twin-lead that is optimistically called a "dipole-fm antenna."

Before discussing individual types of antennas for fm use, some fundamental facts must be established. First, fm transmission is basically a "line-of-sight" operation, much like TV.

The so-called "ionosphere," responsible for long distance reception of medium and "short-wave" transmissions, is virtually useless in the vhf region associated with fm and TV transmission. On the basis of this fact, a formula can be derived for approximate range of transmission, considering only the fact that the horizon limits the distance. In simplified form, the formula boils down to:

$$d = 1.23 \ (\sqrt{h})$$

where,
    d is distance in miles,
    h is the height of transmitting tower in feet.

Typically, then, a 1000-ft transmitting tower will have a "visibility distance" to the horizon of approximately 40 miles. The foregoing formula assumes that the receiver is at "ground level." It has been found, however, that signals are received beyond the horizon, to some extent. This phenomenon is explained by two causes: refraction in the lower atmosphere and diffraction of the electromagnetic waves by the surface of the earth at the horizon. A good approximation of this added range may be obtained by modifying the formula to read: $d = 1.41 \sqrt{h}$, so that our 1000-ft transmitter tower might now be expected to cause reception at distances of approximately 45 miles, still at ground level. If the receiving antenna is also located above ground level, however, the range can be further increased. The new formula for this case becomes:

$$d = 1.41 \ (\sqrt{h_t} + \sqrt{h_r})$$

where,
    h_t is the height of the transmitter antenna,
    h_r is the height of the receiving antenna.

Here we see one of the reasons why an outdoor roof antenna is inherently a better arrangement than the same antenna placed "under the rug" at ground level. In the example previously cited, an apartment house dweller able to mount his receiving antenna at a height of 100 ft might be expected to increase basic range of fm reception (at a given signal strength) from 45 miles to approximately 59 miles.

Of course, many other factors are involved in selecting the type of antenna to be used, and these cannot be generalized but must be evaluated in terms of individual needs.

Half-wave Folded Dipole

Perhaps the most popular type of antenna used for fm reception is the half-wave dipole. As shown in Fig. 3-1, it strongly resembles the early, popular TV antennas. For this reason, perhaps, many fm listeners couple their fm sets right to their previously installed TV antennas. This practice, while better than most 'indoor" arrangements, is deficient in two very important respects. For one thing, the long dipole element of a TV antenna is usually cut to a frequency of around 50 or 60 MHz. To compute the length of a half-wave antenna use formula:

$$L = \frac{468}{f}$$

where,
L is the length in feet,
f is the frequency in MHz.

Thus, the TV antenna is probably about 8 ft long, whereas a properly cut fm antenna, tuned to midband of about 100 MHz, should be 4.68 ft long.

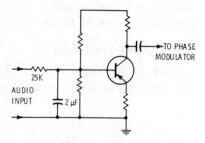

Fig. 3-6. Corrective network for attenuating high frequencies that might affect fm output.

An antenna will exhibit greatest gain at or near its resonant frequency. Also, the simultaneous use of a TV antenna for TV and fm results in a mismatch and consequent reduction in available signal strength at the fm antenna terminals of the receiver. If a proper two-set coupler is used, the mismatch is less severe, but some attenuation of available signal still occurs.

As for the characteristics of the standard half-wave folded dipole shown in Fig. 3-7, it has a bidirectional receiving pattern. That is, it receives signals from stations that are perpendicular to the bars either from front or back. In the days of monophonic fm, it was considered adequate for signals up to about 30 miles away. Unfortunately, stereo fm is much more demanding and critical than is mono fm. For one thing, stereo fm takes about *five times* the signal strength for noise-free reception equal to mono fm.

Fig. 3-7. Simple, half-wave folded dipole.

This is not the fault of the receiver; rather, it is an inborn characteristic of the transmitted signal itself. In addition, reflected waves reaching the antenna are apt to cause phase shifts in portions of the received signals which can not only cause distortion (identified by hissing or sibilant "s" sounds in speech) but, in extreme cases, can all but destroy the stereo separation effect.

It is obvious, therefore, that for all but ideal conditions, the half-wave folded dipole should be discarded in favor of a more *directional* type of antenna array.

Folded Dipole With Reflector

This simple form of receiving antenna, illustrated in Fig. 3-8, has a more unidirectional pattern since it receives stations

Fig. 3-8. Folded dipole with reflector.

best from in front of the dipole. It is most useful in situations where most stations desired are in the same general direction. This might be true for the "near-suburbanite" who wishes to receive stations from his nearby, metropolitan location.

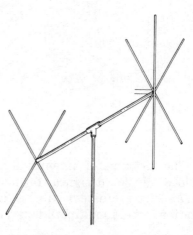

Fig. 3-9. Conical antenna.

Conical, Turnstile and "S" Types

The antenna configuration shown in Fig. 3-9 has the same directional response as a simple dipole. It is useful, however, when stereo stations are located at both the low and high ends of the fm dial since its frequency response is somewhat broader than that of a simple dipole. Of course, if multipath (reflection) problems are present in a particular installation, it is insufficiently directional to counter these effects.

Turnstile Antenna

The antenna shown in Fig. 3-10 is also called a cross-dipole antenna because it consists of two bidirectional elements

Fig. 3-10. "Turnstile" or cross-dipole antenna.

mounted at right angles. The omnidirectional pattern obtained allows reception from local stations in various directions. This antenna is particularly useful when the user is located in "close-in suburbs" *between* two cities and is not plagued by the presence of multipath-causing high steel structures, mountainous terrain, etc.

Fig. 3-11. Multielement Yagi antenna.

The "S" type of antenna is another variant of the simple folded dipole, designed to make it more omnidirectional. Again, its usefulness will be limited to reception of nearby stations where multipath is not a serious problem.

Unidirectional FM Antennas

For fringe area reception of fm and stereo fm, a high-gain, directional antenna is imperative to enjoy excellent reception. The two most popular types in this category are the multi-element Yagi and the newer, log-periodic. A diagram of the Yagi is shown in Fig. 3-11 while a typical log-periodic antenna is illustrated in Fig. 3-12. Both of these antenna types feature

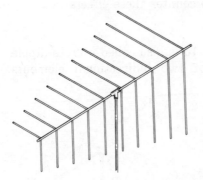

Fig. 3-12. "Log-periodic" fm antenna.

high gain and a very narrow angle of directivity. Stereo reception at distances up to 75 miles is not uncommon with a sensitive fm receiver and a properly installed antenna of either of these two types. Of course, the narrow angle of reception means that the antenna must be well oriented during installation and, if stations are located in various directions, antennas of these types must be installed with one of the many electrically operated rotators currently available.

Boosters

In addition to directional high gain antennas, some experts recommend the use of a booster or preamplifier for extreme fringe-area reception of stereo fm. A booster is really nothing more than a preamplifier. Most of the commercially available units employ one or more solid-state devices to act as the amplifying elements (sometimes field-effect transistors). On the surface, one would think that more amplification in the form of such a pre-rf stage would always enhance performance, but this is not true. Modern receivers (at least the more sensitive ones) have noise figures which are often *lower* than the inherent noise figures of the store-bought boosters. In fm, it is the signal-to-noise ratio that counts, not just the number of signal microvolts available at the input to the receiver. Thus, if a given booster amplifies noise as well as signal, nothing is really gained in overall performance. On the other hand, a well designed rf preamplifier or booster can work wonders if used in conjunction with a less expensive or less sensitive receiver that has an inferior noise figure to begin with.

Summary

All too often, we encounter stereo installations in which the fm tuner or receiver is a high-priced, quality unit capable of excellent performance, but is denied a satisfactory signal through inadequate consideration of antenna needs. The cost of even a good antenna is quite moderate, compared to the cost of a fine tuner or receiver. It is not unusual to measure improvements of ten-to-one in signal strength reaching the receiver once an adequate antenna is used, compared with the "hunk of wire under the rug" approach—so why deny a good piece of equipment a decent input signal (and yourself optimum reception)?

Chapter 4

FM Front Ends

RF FRONT ENDS

Having examined some general characteristics of fm in preceding chapters, we are now ready to begin a step-by-step analysis of the "blocks" used to make up a typical, high-quality fm tuner.

First, let's define the word "tuner," because it means different things to different people. In high-fidelity terminology, the "tuner" is all the circuitry needed to convert the received signal at the fm antenna into audio information suitable for application to an audio amplifier. "Package" or console manufacturers often refer to a "tuner" too, but they mean just the early portion of the receiver devoted to amplifying the radio frequencies and converting them to an intermediate frequency of 10.7 MHz. It is this section of a "tuner" that we call a "front-end"; and it is this section to which we shall now devote our attention.

Fig. 4-1 is a block diagram of a typical "tuner" (by our definition). The shaded block is the one we will study first.

Today's tuners almost invariably employ solid-state amplifying devices in the front end, as well as in the i-f section. More recently, many manufacturers are using field-effect transistors in at least the rf stage of the front end. These solid-state devices more nearly approximate the performance of the highly perfected rf tube designs that were popular a few years ago. If this seems a bit paradoxical, one must realize that the pressures of marketing forced designers into complete transistorization a bit too soon. Only now are the solid-state devices used for front-end design catching up with some basic performance capabilities long associated with vacuum-tube performance. For this reason, we shall first examine an "old fashioned" cascode rf amplifier, as used in a certain radio receiver some years back.

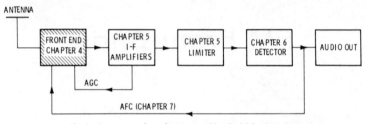

Fig. 4-1. Block diagram of an fm tuner. Shaded block indicates section discussed here.

The ability of a receiver to amplify a signal is not limited by the amplification attainable from the vacuum tubes or transistors, but rather by the noise which arises from these devices and their associated circuitry. Further, the noise developed in this first rf stage is actually the most significant: whatever noise voltage appears at the grid of this stage will be amplified along with the signal. The best choice for low noise (confining the discussion to tubes, for the moment) is a triode amplifier tube. Unfortunately, the gain of most triodes is less than that obtainable from pentode tubes.

The circuit shown in Fig. 4-2, known as a cascode amplifier, combines the gain features of a pentode with the low-noise features associated with triode operation. L1 and L2 constitutes a matching transformer arrangement known as a "balun." While most antenna transmission lines used for home fm receivers are the familiar 300-ohm twin-lead type, coaxial transmission line has been shown to be more advantageous when fighting local man-made noise, such as ignition from vehicles, etc. Coaxial transmission line sold for this purpose has an impedance of 72 ohms, and if no provision were made for impedance match, the signal lost by virtue of the mismatch to a 300-ohm receiver input might well offset the gains resulting from the use of coaxial lines in the first place. Some high-quality sets provide inputs matched for *either* 72 or 300 ohms for this reason.

The signal from secondary L2 is applied to the first tuned circuit, which in turn connects to the control grid of the first triode section. The signal at the plate of the first triode is coupled to the *cathode* of the second triode section, while the grid of the second triode is grounded (so far as rf is concerned). Thus, the first stage is operated as a conventional amplifier, while the second stage is employed as a grounded-grid amplifier.

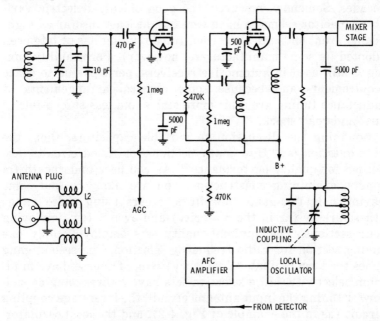

Fig. 4-2. Good-quality front end from the vacuum-tube era, featuring a popular "cascode" dual-triode rf stage of the period.

The nondetailed blocks (local oscillator and mixer) constitute the rest of this "front end"; operation of these blocks will be discussed in more detail later. At this point, however, before we present analogous transistorized stages, it would be well to examine some of the other features of this first section of an fm tuner. For one thing, we glossed over the means of tuning.

47

Tuning is generally accomplished by means of a variable air capacitor, much like those used in a-m receivers. Over the years many other schemes of tuning or changing frequency have been devised. For example, coaxial variable capacitors were tried by one manufacturer some years ago. Instead of the plates meshing, as in a conventional capacitor, a coaxial capacitor consists of a stationary cylinder into which is plunged a movable cylinder. The two are separated by a dielectric (usually a glass cylinder, onto which the outer conductive plate is heat shrunk or vacuum plated).

Permeability tuning (where the inductance rather than the capacitance of the resonant circuits is varied) in various forms has also been used in a great many designs over the past two decades. Somehow, however, the good old air-dielectric variable capacitor seems to have won out, at least insofar as high-fidelity front ends are concerned (diode tuning has of late been adopted by some manufacturers, however). Permeability tuning is still used in automotive receivers, perhaps due to space requirements and because some physical arrangements of inductance tuning are a bit more stable and less susceptible to dust and road shock.

Confining the discussion to variable capacitors, then, the next question is: "How many sections, or tuned circuits, are needed for quality performance?" As you peer underneath fm tuners, examining construction, you are likely to find some having only two-gang capacitors, others using three gangs (these are by far in the majority) and even a few employing four sections. The minimal-quality sets employing only one tuning section for radio frequency selection (the second gang tunes the local oscillator frequency) will, of course, have minimum selectivity. More selective sets have a three-gang capacitor for tuning the input antenna circuit, the interstage coupling circuit (as in the example of Fig. 4-2), and the local oscillator. Four-gang capacitors will be found in sets which employ more than one rf stage or in designs where the interstage coupling is accomplished by means of a double-tuned circuit.

Agc or "automatic gain control" is often applied to the rf stage to prevent overload of the stage when particularly strong signals are applied. This means that the first stage must have the capability of exhibiting varying gain with different bias settings. This was easily accomplished with "variable mu" vacuum tubes and is equally easy to accomplish with today's transistors, which depend on bias for varying figures of gain. Note that this feature is called automatic gain control, rather than avc (automatic volume control), the term used in a-m receivers. This is because changing the *amplitude* of the rf signal in an fm reciver does alter the volume or "loudness" of the resultant output unless we are speaking of signals so weak that they do not cause full limiting in subsequent i-f stages.

Other features of an fm stage which are not apparent from examining the schematic alone should be noted. Coils represented in the usual manner in the schematic become just four or five turns of heavy wire, with rather large spacing between turns, often using air as a dielectric. The variable capacitor sections themselves usually have just two or three plates in the rotor or stator, since we are dealing with total capacitances of just a few picofarads. Dress and layout of parts are much more critical than in a-m rf stages, because even an inch or so of excess wire length implies a significant amount of additional inductance. Proper grounding is very important, too.

The techniques used to design and lay out rf sections of an fm receiver have evolved over a great many years. It is not the sort of thing a novice kit-builder should attempt to do from simple referral to a schematic. It is for this reason, incidentally, that most tuner kit manufacturers supply the front end in preassembled form, often even prealigned. To really appreciate the differences between a broadcast-band rf design and one intended for fm reception, you should examine the front-end construction of an fm tuner. Note the overall shielding (good fm tuners usually enclose the entire front end in a metal shield—to preclude excessive radiation from the local oscillator and to prevent accidental or intentional tampering with precisely-aligned coils, trimmers, etc.).

RF FRONT ENDS GO "SOLID STATE"

It is sad but true that early attempts at rf front-end transistorization resulted in performance that was measurably inferior to the tube designs displaced. While the author does not wish to belabor the overenthusiasm of the industry in rushing into solid-state front-end designs, a brief discussion of why these first designs fell short of the mark will help in understanding some vital fm rf design considerations.

There are several things that an rf stage is expected to do, in terms of overall fm performance. For one, it is expected to establish a suitably low noise figure. Since the rf incoming signal is at its lowest level at the input to this critical first stage, it is this first rf stage which ultimately determines overall noise figure. Another characteristic expected of an rf stage is satisfactory selectivity. In general, the rf stage will be tuned (either double-tuned at input and output, or single-tuned at output) to provide as much selectivity as possible without restricting necessary channel bandwidth. An rf stage may be expected to encounter signal input levels ranging from a few microvolts to a volt or more—in other words, a dynamic range approaching one million! If the stage is to handle this range without overload, some means must be provided to vary the gain of the active device, be it tube, Nuvistor, transistor, or FET (field effect transistor). Such variation, as mentioned earlier, is accomplished by means of an automatic gain control (agc) voltage. Finally, a good rf stage should produce a minimum of spurious responses of its own and be subject to a minimum of interference brought about by certain combinations of multiple frequencies related to but not identified with the desired signal frequency.

With all of the preceding requirements in mind, let us examine a typical early rf stage attempting to use high-frequency germanium transistors for an rf amplifying circuit. The circuit is shown schematically in Fig. 4-3. The first big

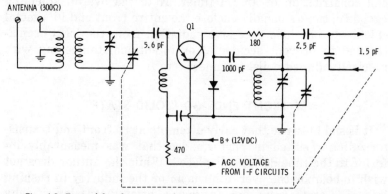

Fig. 4-3. Typical fm rf stage employing an ordinary bipolar pnp transistor.

problem here is that, in the common-base configuration, input impedance of a bipolar germanium transistor is quite low. If the input is pretuned with a parallel tank circuit, one of two detrimental things will happen: (1) If we just place the tank circuit across the input, it will load it down, reducing circuit Q and selectivity; (2) If we compensate for the basic impedance mismatch, and "tap down" on the tank circuit, we will be tapping down on the signal voltage, or reducing gain capability.

To make matters worse, agc, while present in the circuit of Fig. 4-3, is limited in its action by the gain-changing characteristics of the typical bipolar transistor. These devices are limited in dynamic range and, therefore, could be subjected to overload even in the presence of carefully worked out agc schemes.

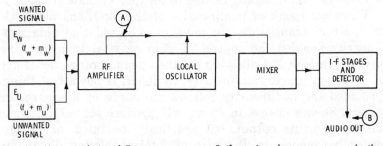

Fig. 4-4. Unwanted signal E_u may appear at B if receiver has poor a-m rejection and/or poor i-f limiting.

With operating points established along the nonlinear characteristics of the transistor (to enable gain control), several forms of spurious response were often present. The two most important spurious responses that plagued early transistorized front-end designs were cross-modulation and intermodulation distortions. Cross-modulation distortion can occur when a receiver is tuned to a small, wanted signal (E_w), while a large, unwanted signal (E_u) causes interference. With poor selectivity, the large signal is usually within the range of selectivity of the rf stage.

Fig. 4-4 shows the wanted and unwanted signals as inputs to the rf amplifier. E_w consists of carrier frequency f_w and modulation frequency m_w. E_u consists of carrier frequency f_u and modulating frequency m_u. When E_u is very large with respect to E_w, an actual transfer of modulation, m_u from f_u to f_w, is accomplished because of the nonlinear input of the rf amplifier stage. The output waveform contains $f_w + m_w + m_u$ instead of the desired $f_w + m_w$ only. The amplified signal at A may contain the desired carrier plus modulation of both desired and undesired carriers if a strong unwanted signal is close in frequency to a weak, wanted signal.

Intermodulation distortion occurs when two or more frequencies, related in a particular way (so far as frequency only is concerned) are applied to the nonlinear transfer characteristic of such an rf amplifier. The resultant frequencies present after the intermodulation process must be related harmonically to the center frequency of the tuner and the local oscillator frequency to produce a measurable amount of intermediate frequency or its subharmonics; or the resultant frequencies must be subharmonically related to the intermediate frequency.

When we speak of nonlinearity of the input characteristic of early rf transistors, we must quickly add that this nonlinearity enabled the control of gain so vital in preventing severe overload and allowing for the dynamic range necessary in an fm rf stage. Nonlinearity, by itself, is not a bad thing, provided the nonlinearity follows the curve of a square-law device. Such a device, in effect, will produce second-harmonic distortion in its output, but practically no third- or higher-order harmonics. In the case of intermodulation distortion, second-harmonic distortion corresponds to first order (or sum and difference) intermodulation products. Thus, if one signal is 103 MHz and the other is 104 MHz, the sum will be 207 MHz and the difference will be 1 MHz. Neither of these products is anywhere near the selective range of the mixer or i-f stages that follow. Consequently there is no problem. Still, gain control is made possible because of the nonlinear characteristic still present.

The up-to-date circuit of Fig. 4-5 illustrates the use of a field-effect transistor (FET) in the critical rf stage. This device fills the square law requirement, and does a lot more, too. Unlike the bipolar transistor, the input impedance at the gate element is very high—higher, in fact, than was the grid input impedance of the old triode vacuum tube. (Incidentally, the elements of the FET are called *gate*, *drain* and *source*. The gate is the controlling element, similar in function to the grid

52

of a vacuum tube. Sometimes the drain and source, equivalent to a tube's plate and cathode, may be physically interchanged with no difference in performance of the device. Many forms of FET's are appearing on the market, and it is beyond the scope of this book to detail differences between the various types.)

This high input impedance enables us to resort to classical high-impedance resonant-circuit coupling at the input, improving selectivity while at the same time permitting full, useful gain of the device to be realized. The improved selectivity, coupled with the square-law action of the FET's has resulted in cross-modulation rejection of nearly 100 dB! Such

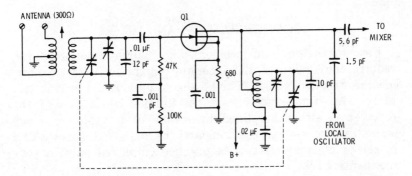

Fig. 4-5. Modern amplifier design using an FET device. Note the similarity to a triode amplifier circuit.

superior rejection exceeds rejection figures typical of tube circuits, which generally run about 80 or 85 dB. Certainly, it surpasses anything that was possible with conventional bipolar transistors, where typical cross-modulation figures ran 60 to 70 dB!

You may recall that we discussed equivalent thermal noise in early tube or transistor stages of an fm receiver. The equivalent noise resistance is, in effect, a fictitious resistor connected in series with the input of the rf amplifier. This equivalent resistance determines the ultimate noise figure of the front end. In the case of a typical triode, the equivalent noise resistance (simplified from a more complex formula) reduces to $2.5/G_m$, where G_m is the transconductance of the tube. Thus, a triode having a G_m of 8,000 micromhos would have an equivalent noise resistance of approximately 310 ohms. The 2.5 figure is used because a triode operates at a temperature which is about 2.5 *times* as high as room temperature, when both are expressed in the absolute (Kelvin) scale. Room temperature is about 300K, whereas tube operation is at about 750K. The ratio of the two is, therefore, 2.5.

Since a transistor (and that includes an FET) operates at just about room temperature, the equivalent noise resistance becomes $1/G_m$, rather than $2.5/G_m$, so that an FET having a transconductance of 8000 micromhos would represent an equivalent noise resistance of only about 125 ohms, and the lower the equivalent noise resistance, the better the noise figure!

LOCAL OSCILLATORS AND MIXERS

Fm superheterodyne receivers, like their a-m counterparts, require conversion of the incoming signal to a lower intermediate frequency (i-f). The i-f almost universally used is 10.7 MHz. The signal received at the antenna terminals of the receiver is either amplified by means of a radio-frequency stage, as discussed in previous articles, or is fed directly to a mixer or converter stage (a practice employed only in very inexpensive sets).

The terms "mixer" and "converter" are not synonymous, even though they are often used interchangeably. A converter will involve the use of a tube or transistor which produces an oscillator voltage *and* mixes this voltage with the incoming rf signal. A mixer, on the other hand, fulfills only one of the above functions—the beating together of the incoming signal with a separately produced oscillator voltage. At the relatively low a-m band frequencies it has become almost standard practice to use a converter stage. At signal frequencies of the fm band, however, operation of the local-oscillator stage becomes more critical. Stability of output voltage is more difficult to achieve and interaction between oscillator and incoming signal voltage is more likely to occur with converters. While this does not rule out the use of converters in fm receivers (see Fig. 4-6), all but the most inexpensive units will separate the mixer and oscillator functions by using individual devices (tubes or transistors) for each.

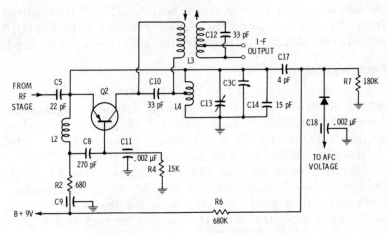

Fig. 4-6. Example of low-cost fm rf front-end "converter."

Tubes versus Transistors

In examining the various circuits which compose an fm tuner or receiver, it is our practice to examine performance of these circuits in terms of relative advantages and disadvantages as the state of the art has advanced from tubes to solid-state circuitry. Accordingly, we shall first examine a high-quality tube-type oscillator circuit, followed by a modern transistorized local oscillator.

The first of these circuits is shown in Fig. 4-7. It is the local-oscillator circuit of a Fisher Radio Model 500-C. Oscillation is achieved by the feedback circuit involving C22 (plate to grid circuit); resonant frequency is determined by the tank circuit consisting of L4, C8C, C19, C24 and C25. The variable capacitor section (C8C), along with its rf sections, is used to vary

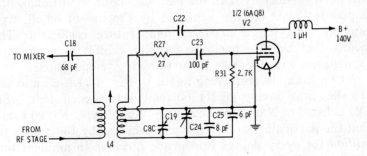

Fig. 4-7. Local oscillator circuit (Fisher 500-C receiver).

55

the oscillator frequency so that it is always 10.7 MHz removed from the received incoming signal. Trimmer capacitor C19 permits optimization of frequency tracking across the fm band.

Frequency Stability

Frequency conversion and the whole superheterodyne concept depends on beating an incoming frequency against an accurately maintained local oscillator frequency to produce an accurate intermediate frequency. Transmitter channel accuracy is maintained and safeguarded by many electronic techniques (not to mention the surveillance of the FCC). At the receiving end, therefore, the accuracy of the intermediate frequency will depend primarily upon the frequency stability of the local oscillator. A drift of only 1 percent at 100 MHz represents a shift of 100 kHz, enough to shift the converted signal partially or completely outside the range of the tuned i-f stages which follow.

Heat that is generated in a tube-type receiver (from tubes, transformers and even resistors) is largely responsible for oscillator drift, and 1 percent or even 2 percent is the magnitude of drift you might typically expect if certain design precautions were not taken. Increased temperature causes an increase in *both* coil inductance and capacitor capacitance. It is for this reason that drift in an fm tuner will always be *downward* in frequency, since resonant frequency varies inversely with the square root of both inductance and capacitance.

Proper precautions, such as careful layout of components, which permits air to circulate and positions heat-producing elements far away from critical inductances and capacitances, will partly reduce drift in the local oscillator. Additional, final compensation is usually achieved by the use of small, fixed capacitors having a *negative* temperature coefficient. This means that these capacitors actually exhibit a *decrease* in capacitance with increase in surrounding temperature.

As an example (referring again to Fig. 4-7), C22 and C23 are shown as having an N1500 temperature coefficient, while C24 is listed at N330, and C25 is an "NPO" type. N1500 means that the particular capacitance will decrease by 1500 parts per *million* for every degree centigrade *increase* in ambient temperature. Similarly, N330 means a decrease in 330 parts per million (of capacitance) for each degree centigrade increase in temperature. "NPO" means negative-positive-zero—or, a temperature-stable capacitor that neither increases nor decreases in capacitance with temperature changes. Less expensive design would have attempted to stabilize frequency with only *one* temperature-compensating capacitor in the resonant circuit. By using both an N330 and an NPO type for C24 and C25, the circuit achieves precisely the compensation desired during the short-term and long-term drift time period.

Fig. 4-8 illustrates typical drift conditions for compensated and uncompensated oscillator designs. Other measures taken

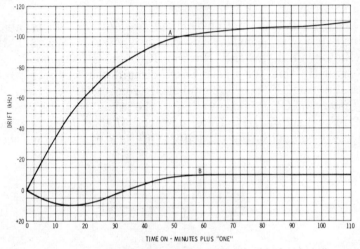

Fig. 4-8. Uncompensated and heat-compensated drift of fm local oscillators.

to provide frequency stability include regulation of power supply voltage (oscillator frequency will vary with change of supply voltage) and design of resonant circuits in such a way that internal tube capacitances are a negligible percentage of the total capacitance present across the tuning circuit. This last requirement is necessary because, during tube warmup, the internal capacitance of a tube changes. Oscillator voltage coupling to the mixer tube (the other half of the 6AQ8 tube) is accomplished inductively, by means of a secondary winding on coil L4. In many other designs (both transistor and tube), coupling is achieved by means of a very small capacitor (often just a few pF in value).

SOLID-STATE OSCILLATORS

Not very long ago, the designers of fm receivers were not so much concerned with *which* transistor to use as a local oscillator in fm sets, but rather with the problem of getting *any* transistors which would oscillate at frequencies in the vicinity of 100 MHz. Today, of course, many types are available for the purpose, each with minimal input and output capacitances and with sufficiently high cut-off frequency to permit oscillation at the required frequencies. Furthermore, the battle against drift is much simplified because the amount of heat produced by all-transistor fm tuners is very much less than that associated with tube sets.

Lest you get the notion that *all* precautions can be abandoned, however, consider the design shown in Fig. 4-9, the oscillator used in the Harman-Kardon SR900 solid-state receiver. In this "grounded base" circuit, the feedback which sustains oscillation is accomplished from collector to emitter by means of C4, while coupling to the mixer stage is through a 2-pF capacitor, C11. Note, however, that at least one temperature-compensating capacitor, C13, is still used since there

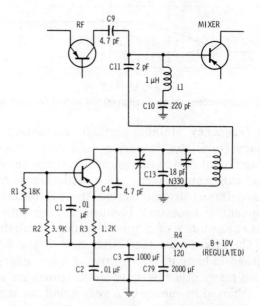

Fig. 4-9. Local oscillator in the Harman-Kardon SR-900, fm section.

is still some increase in chassis temperature with warm-up of output transistor heat-sinks and other components in the chassis.

Examination of the power supply section of this receiver discloses that the 10-volt (positive) supply required by the oscillator stage is zener-diode regulated to prevent variations in line voltage from affecting oscillator frequency.

In a-m receivers intended for the broadcast band and utilizing an i-f of 455 kHz, positioning of the oscillator frequency *above* the incoming signal is dictated from practical design considerations. Since the broadcast band extends from 535 to 1605 kHz, placing the local oscillator frequency *below* the incoming signal would mean having an oscillator frequency range from 80 kHz to 1150 kHz. This represents a tuning ratio of nearly 15 to 1 and, therefore, a variable capacitance end-to-end capacitance ratio of nearly 225 to 1. This is hardly practical, physically.

With fm, however, the case is not so one sided. With the fm band extending from 88 to 108 MHz and the i-f desired set to 10.7 MHz, oscillator frequency range could be set either from 77.3 to 97.3 MHz or from 98.7 to 118.7 MHz. Either range is practical from a design point of view. If the lower frequencies had been selected, as a matter of fact, design would be somewhat simpler in terms of attaining frequency stability, ease of construction and the use of somewhat less critical components. Unfortunately, TV channels 5 (76-82 MHz) and 6 (82-88 MHz) fall right in the range of the lower frequency alternative and, although shielding of local oscillators to prevent excessive radiation is a requirement of the FCC, it would not take much such radiation to interfere with one's own TV set (particularly if a common antenna is used). For this reason, nearly all fm sets produced today utilize a local oscillator tuned to the *higher* set of frequencies. An indirect advantage of this choice is the somewhat reduced tuning ratio this requires.

AFC AND OSCILLATOR STABILITY

While we shall deal in much greater detail with afc (automatic frequency control) in Chapter 7, there is one point on the subject that needs to be made here. To those unfamiliar with afc and how it works, a brief explanation of Fig. 4-10 will suffice. In this schematic, the oscillator section of the Eico Model 3200 tuner is shown. The diode component identified as FECR2, in series with a 15-pF capacitor, is effectively in shunt with part of the frequency-determining tuned circuit of the local-oscillator stage. This diode acts like a small variable capacitor when varying dc voltages are applied to it.

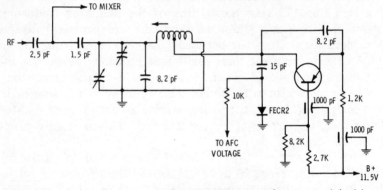

Fig. 4-10. Local-oscillator section of EICO 3200 tuner. Afc is accomplished by voltage-tuned diode.

Both popular forms of detector circuit used for fm demodulation (the ratio detector and the Foster-Seeley discriminator) produce negative and positive dc voltages as stations are detuned above or below center frequency. These voltages are used as error-correcting voltages by causing a corrective shift in local-oscillator frequency. This corrective scheme may be thought of as a first-order servo loop and, as such, cannot be expected to offer total correction since some finite amount of error must be present for the corrective frequency shift to occur.

The real purpose of the afc is to make it somewhat easier for the user to tune in stations. With afc, stations "pop in" and stay fairly well tuned (though not perfectly so). Notwithstanding the advertising slogans, afc does not, of itself, provide drift-free tuning. It is *not* a substitute for a frequency-stable oscillator design. On the contrary, afc often shows up a drifting oscillator even more. The user often thinks he is tuned to center of channel (in the absence of a good tuning meter) and actually may be on the edge of "drop-out" of the desired channel. Most instruction manuals prescribe that desired stations be tuned in with the afc turned off (if it is defeatable). Only after center-of-channel has been tuned in properly should afc be introduced.

Many manufacturers have eliminated afc altogether, claiming (and rightly so, in our opinion) that equally smooth tuning action can be obtained through the use of wideband i-f designs. They further maintain that all but the most carefully designed afc schemes contribute a measure of distortion to the output and that, since afc is really no true substitute for oscillator stability, it serves little or no purpose in modern, stable, solid-state fm designs. Ten years ago, absence of afc circuitry was a mark of "skimping" in design. Today, it is fast becoming a mark of distinction when accompanied by good wideband design.

Chapter 5

I-F Amplifiers and Limiters

I-F AMPLIFIERS

There are so many factors to be considered in discussing fm i-f performance, design, and desired specifications, that an entire book might be devoted to this subject alone. All we can hope to do in a quick treatment is to acquaint the reader with some of the high points of design and operation of this most vital section of an fm tuner or receiver.

The need for an i-f section arises from the use of the super-heterodyne principle common to both a-m and fm equipment. By reducing all incoming signal frequencies to a single, lower frequency (by the conversion or mixing process discussed in Chapter 4), subsequent amplification is relatively simpler and more stable, and reliable designs can be produced. Actually, the lower the intermediate frequency, the easier it is to come up with an effective design. Why, then, did the industry choose 10.7 MHz as the universally accepted i-f for fm, as opposed to, say, 455 kHz (used for a-m i-f stages) or some other low frequency? For one thing, such a small spread between local oscillator frequency and incoming signal frequency might well cause a strong incoming signal to "pull" the frequency of the local oscillator, until both were "locked" at the same frequency. Result: no i-f output from the converter for the i-f stages to amplify! Still, an intermediate frequency of a couple of megahertz would eliminate this problem. So why 10.7 MHz?

Well, suppose, for the moment, that we were to choose an i-f of 4.5 MHz (as is, in fact, done for the sound portion of some TV receivers), and suppose we were tuned to a signal frequency of 95.0 MHz. If the oscillator were designed to operate *above* incoming frequency, it would be oscillating at 99.5 MHz. Next, assume there were another station (and a strong one at that) in the vicinity, transmitting at a frequency of 104MHz. Despite the selectivity of the tuned rf stage (assuming there *is* one), this higher frequency would beat with the 99.5 MHz of the local oscillator to produce a second signal, also at 4.5 MHz. Before you decide that the local oscillator should have been designed to operate *below* the incoming signal frequency, take a look at Fig. 5-1B, which shows that the same thing can happen, only this time with the desired stations at the high end of the dial and the undesired station 9 MHz lower.

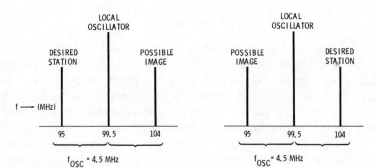

(A) *Local oscillator 4.5 MHz above desired station frequency.*

(B) *Local oscillator 4.5 MHz below desired station frequency.*

Fig. 5-1. Image frequencies in a receiver.

It's pretty obvious, therefore, that given an fm band of 20 MHz (from 88 MHz to 108 MHz), the lowest i-f necessary to avoid image responses would be some frequency greater than 10MHz. The last major consideration which led, specifically, to the choice of 10.7 MHz has to do with "direct i-f response." If some station is transmitting at the chosen intermediate frequency itself, such a received signal could easily reach the i-f circuits either through the usual input channels (which might lack sufficient selectivity to exclude them) or by the appearance of i-f signal voltage directly at the input of the first i-f stage when adequate shielding is not provided. To avoid this possibility, the chosen frequency (10.7 MHz) is one that is never or seldom used for commercial transmission. This choice does not eliminate every type of spurious response possible, but it seems to be the best compromise choice available.

Having established the frequency of the fm i-f strip, we can now consider the additional characteristics which must be considered. They are really surprisingly few in number (though often a design can be quite difficult to achieve). Gain, of course, is one. Bandwidth is another, phase response a third, and that's really about all there are. Remember, we are excluding limiter stages from the discussion, even though many consider them to be part of the i-f strip (structurally, they usually are). We shall deal with limiters and their special additional requirements later.

While you might suppose that a bandwidth of 150 kHz is all that would ever be required of an i-f stage (based upon the maximum allowable modulation of ± 75 kHz), recall that sidebands may actually exist well beyond these superficial limits. This is especially true now, since the advent of stereo fm (multiplex), which involves higher modulating frequencies. A bandwidth of 6 dB (attenuation) for around 250 to 300 kHz is now accepted as being adequate for high quality, stereo fm reception. Ideally, the shape of the response curve of the i-f system should be that shown in Fig. 5-2. Generally, however, the expense involved in attempting to come close to such perfect response is prohibitive. There is at least one manufacturer who comes mighty close to this ideal by means of complex, multiple-section filter networks. Most manufacturers achieve their response by means of double-tuned, interstage i-f transformers, as represented in Fig. 5-3.

Depending upon the number of stages used and the excellence of the particular design, the resultant response curve might be something like that shown in Fig. 5-4. It should be noted that when we speak of a 6-dB loss for a bandwidth of 250 kHz we mean the total attenuation of the entire i-f system, not simply of a single stage. Thus, in the example cited, if there were three tuned circuits in the i-f system, each circuit would

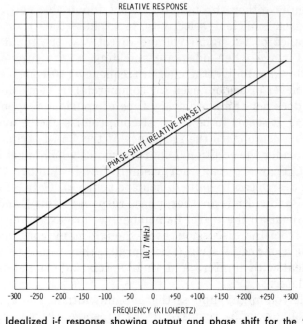

PHASE SHIFT (RELATIVE PHASE)

10.7 MHz)

-300 -250 -200 -150 -100 -50 0 +50 +100 +150 +200 +250 +300

FREQUENCY (KILOHERTZ)

Fig. 5-2. Idealized i-f response showing output and phase shift for the "perfect" i-f system.

contribute 2 dB of attenuation at the "end points," but the total response of the entire system would then be down 6 dB at 250 kHz.

Still another method of achieving a desired bandwidth characteristic involves the use of newly devised crystal and ceramic filters between amplifying stages. Still relatively new in fm use, these mechanical filters are actually already in use in the i-f systems produced by several well-known receiver manufacturers. Rapid progress in this field is sure to occur in the very near future.

All tuned amplifiers exhibit phase shift between secondary current at resonance and secondary currents at frequencies off-resonance. At resonance, this current is in phase with the i-f transformer's secondary voltage. Above resonance, secondary current leads the secondary voltage, while below resonance the

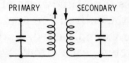

PRIMARY   SECONDARY

Fig. 5-3. Schematic representation of i-f interstage transformer. Arrows indicate "slug" or permeability tuning of both primary and secondary.

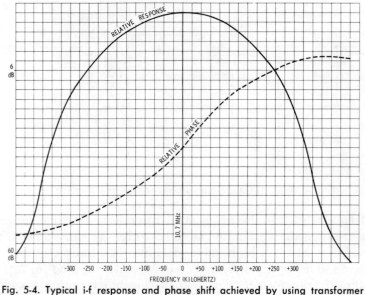

Fig. 5-4. Typical i-f response and phase shift achieved by using transformer coupled circuits.

converse is true. If this phase shift does not vary linearly with changes in frequency within the i-f pass-band, time-delay errors in the received fm signal can occur. Though not terribly serious in monophonic fm reception, such delays can be disastrous in the case of stereo fm, where so much depends upon phase relationships between main-channel audio, 19 kHz pilot sub-carrier, and the stereo sub-carrier information. Proper selection of coefficients of coupling, Q's of the various stages, and required bandwidths helps to achieve a proper frequency/ phase relationship.

Gain in an i-f system (as with any amplifying system) is achieved by means of active amplifying devices, whether tubes, transistors, or integrated-circuit linear amplifiers. A typical i-f stage utilizing a pentode as the active amplifying element is shown in Fig. 5-5. Pentodes were often used because they could be constructed to provide a high transconductance while exhibiting relatively low interelectrode capacitances. In a tuned circuit, a high Q means a high L/C ratio. Thus, if high Q circuits are desired (and they are, for gain and for fashioning desired response curves), we should seek to make L as high as possible. If the C in the picture consists not only of a fixed,

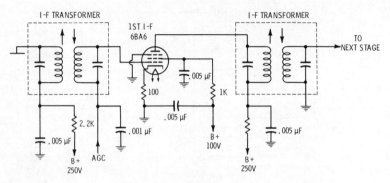

Fig. 5-5. Typical i-f stage using a pentode tube amplifier with agc.

selected value, but also of the stray interelectrode capacitances, we are immediately limited as to how high we can choose L to be. The need for a high value of L also led, indirectly, to the use of inductive tuning rather than capacitive tuning for inter-stage i-f transformers, for with permeability tuning a wider frequency range can be covered without resorting to relatively large variable capacitor values which would again restrict the value of L in the resonant circuit.

The i-f stage illustrated schematically in Fig. 5-6 shows the use of a transistor as the active device. Notice, that because of the low input impedance characteristic of common emitter stages, it becomes necessary to alter the construction of the secondary of the interstage transformer. A tap is brought out near the bottom of the winding to provide a proper impedance

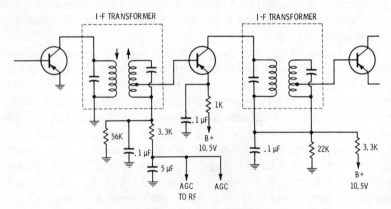

Fig. 5-6. Typical i-f stage using discrete, bipolar transistors.

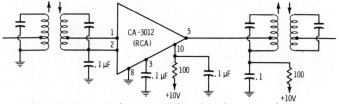

Fig. 5-7. Integrated circuit used in the i-f systems of some present-day fm receivers.

match to the transistor base input and to prevent loading of the entire secondary, with subsequent reduction in Q. Often (though not in the example shown here), even the primary winding is connected to the previous collector by tapping down on the coil, for pretty much the same reason—too low an impedance at the collector output of the previous transistor.

Finally, in Fig. 5-7, we see the use of an integrated circuit in an i-f stage. The contents of this tiny chip stagger the imagination (as shown in Fig. 5-8), for what we see are *ten* transistors, *eleven* resistors and *seven* diodes. What you *don't* immediately see is that not *all* these microscopic devices are contributing directly towards amplification. For example, the triplets Q1-Q2-Q3, Q4-Q5-Q6 and the doublet Q7-Q8 each constitute but a single stage of moderate, though highly stable amplification. Q9 establishes correct bias for the Q7-Q8 doublet, while Q10 and all those diodes act as a voltage regulator for the rest of the circuit.

These wonderful new devices enable construction with fewer external components and, properly employed, they can and are being used in truly great i-f designs, but let us not succumb to the overenthusiastic claims which state ". . . equals ten transistors, nine resistors and umpteen diodes if discrete components were used." At least let's understand what is really meant by such claims. What is *not* needed is a return to the days when tubes were used (often in profusion) as series dropping resistors, so that advertisers could claim radios having "more tubes than anybody."

LIMITERS IN FM RECEIVERS

Strictly speaking, a "limiter" stage in an fm receiver is really another stage in the i-f amplifier section of the receiver.

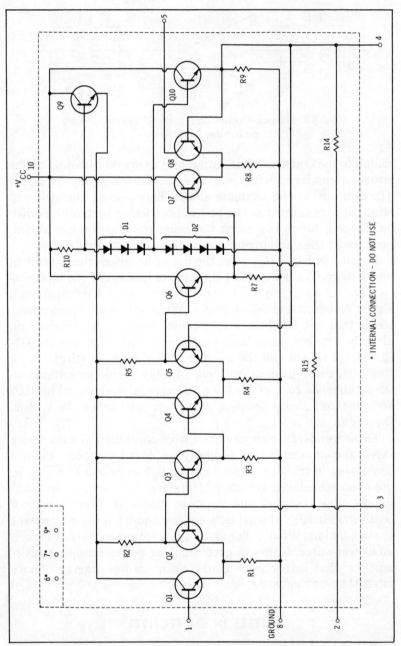

Fig. 5-8. Schematic diagram of the CA3011 or CA3012 integrated-circuit wideband amplifier shown in Fig. 5-7.

Its distinction is that—unlike the stages which precede it—its function is not necessarily one of amplification but rather that of removing amplitude modulation by providing a constant amplitude signal for a rather large range of input signal voltages. The signal frequency is, of course, 10.7 MHz, just as in the rest of the fm i-f system.

If it were possible to design a "perfect" fm detector or demodulator, there would be no need for limiters. As it is, however, all forms of fm detectors (including the popular discriminator and even the ratio-detector types) are, to some degree, sensitive to amplitude as well as to frequency variations in an fm signal. Without the presence of a limiter, the recovered audio output would contain voltages corresponding to both the amplitude and the frequency modulations. A limiter stage (or multiple stages) removes the amplitude-modulation component and passes on a pure frequency-modulated signal

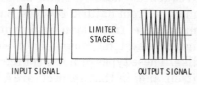

INPUT SIGNAL   OUTPUT SIGNAL

Fig. 5-9. Use of limiter to remove amplitude variations from the fm i-f signal.

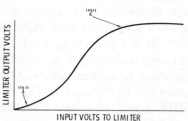

Fig. 5-10. Limiter output curve. Effective limiting occurs at all input signal levels to the right of point 2.

INPUT VOLTS TO LIMITER

for final detection. In general, a discriminator (often called a Foster-Seeley detector, after its inventors) will require a full stage of limiting or more, whereas, a ratio detector, because of its own partial limiting characteristic, is sometimes designed into a set with no limiters ahead of it, often with a partial limiter stage and at other times (in better sets) with a full stage of additional limiting.

A simple illustration of the action of a limiter is shown in Fig. 5-9. A clearer understanding of the functioning of a limiter will be gained by looking at Fig. 5-10, the transfer characteristic of a typical limiter. When applied to this stage, all signals having more than a certain minimum will produce an output voltage which is substantially constant. In the region beginning at point "2" and to the right, the stage is a limiter in its action.

A signal which is too weak to drive the limiter beyond point "2" will cause amplitude variations in the output of this stage (and consequently, in the output of the detector, to a lesser degree) which are not part of the original desired audio information. Thus, for a limiter to operate properly, it is necessary that the incoming signal be strong enough to drive the limiter into full limiting.

You may be wondering how amplitude variations are imparted to an incoming frequency-modulated waveform in the first place. There are two basic causes for this form of distortion. First, there are atmospheric disturbances covering all frequencies used in radio communication. These disturbances may be from natural sources, such as lightning storms, or they may arise from man-made interference such as automobile ignition systems, sparking of electrical motor brushes and the like. These types of noise sources are all external to the receiver itself and, in that respect, are beyond the control of the design engineer. In the receiver proper, unequal response of the various tuned circuits above and below resonance contributes toward amplitude variations. You will recall from the discussion in the preceding chapter that the ideal response curve through an i-f system would be rectangular in shape. Such response is seldom achieved, however; the response is usually more like that shown in Fig. 5-11. A frequency-modulated 10.7-MHz signal fed to an i-f system having such a response will be amplified *more* at the instant the carrier is passing through the center frequency, and somewhat less when deviation caused

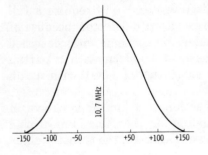

Fig. 5-11. Practical intermediate-frequency response results in varying amplitude as signal is modulated above and below the center frequency.

by audio information shifts the carrier above or below the center frequency (in this case, 10.7 MHz). For effective limiting, the circuit must function beyond the "knee" of its response curve for *all* frequencies that are likely to be encountered under conditions of normal program modulation. For this reason, the limiter has a great influence over the design and selectivity of the preceding i-f stages, as well as upon their degree of amplification.

LIMITER CIRCUITS

The two most widely used circuit schemes for limiting (in the days of vacuum tube equipment) are combined in the typical limiter shown schematically in Fig. 5-12. The RC circuit

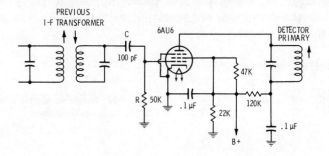

Fig. 5-12. Typical tube limiter using grid-leak bias and reduced plate and screen voltages.

consisting of a 100-pF capacitor and a 50k-ohm resistor from a grid-bias network which, in the presence of an incoming signal, sets the bias point of the grid at some negative value, determined by the amplitude of the signal. Thus, a given amplitude of output is determined by the bias point. If the incoming signal were to undergo a sudden increase in amplitude, the developed grid-leak bias would increase, lowering the effective gain of the stage or, to put it another way, attempting to keep the amplitude of the output *constant*. Unfortunately, the time constant of this arrangement is such that high-frequency amplitude variations are too fast for the grid-leak bias to adjust. As a result, this form of limiting is not very effective in reducing the effects of sharp impulses of noise, such as those arising from automobile ignition systems. The time constant of the bias circuit is determined by the numerical product of the R and C elements in the grid circuit. In this instance, $t = 100 \times 10^{-12}$ (farad) $\times 50,000$ (ohms) $= 5 \times 10^{-6}$ seconds. For most amplitude variations encountered, such time constant will be adequate. In the case of sharp pulses such as ignition noise, even 1- or 2-microsecond time constants may be too slow for the bias to follow, and noise results in the output of the detector which follows.

In addition to grid-circuit limiting, the circuit of Fig. 5-12 utilizes limiting action brought about by reduced plate and screen voltages. Such reduced voltages alter the normal transfer characteristic in such a way that much less input signal is required to drive the plate current into saturation. With a tube (or with a transistor, as we shall soon see) operating in a saturated mode, sharp positive pulses applied to the grid do not alter the amplitude of the output waveform. This is, after all, a form of limiting.

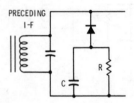

Fig. 5-13. Simplified diagram of a dynamic limiter.

A dynamic limiter overcomes the inability of the grid-bias type to follow high-frequency amplitude variations. Utilizing semiconductor diodes (one or more) that respond instantly to amplitude variations, the dynamic limiter has an RC circuit which holds its characteristic constant with regard to audio variations but permits relatively slower changes to adjust the signal level. A simplified circuit of dynamic limiting is shown in Fig. 5-13. Many experts maintain that the combination of a dynamic limiter followed by a well designed ratio detector afford the best results obtainable in an fm tuner or receiver. Of course, solid-state limiters, including IC (integrated-circuit) stages have changed some of the design philosophy of limiters, but the end goals remain the same.

An example of a transistorized partial limiting stage is shown in Fig. 5-14. Unless you had the rest of the i-f circuitry before you it would be difficult for you to know, for sure, that

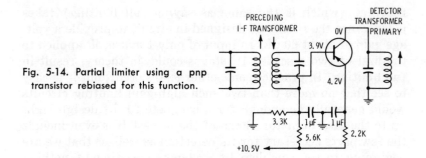

Fig. 5-14. Partial limiter using a pnp transistor rebiased for this function.

the stage is operating as a limiter. The key lies in the operating voltages. While the preceding stage had an emitter-to-collector potential of 9.8V, here the voltage is only 4.2. Essentially, we have saturation limiting translated to solid-state circuitry. Since this stage is followed by a conventional ratio detector (which affords some limiting, too), the limiting is only partial, the rest of the required action being provided by the action of the ratio detector itself.

The principal advantage of the new IC's designed for fm i-f use is that they can be used as amplifiers as well as for limiting purposes. In Fig. 5-8 an RCA CA-3012 was shown used in an i-f circuit. A second such IC, cascaded after the first one and operating with virtually the same voltages operates as a very stiff and effective limiter above certain required input voltages. This limiting action is illustrated graphically in Fig. 5-15. Note that with an input voltage of only about 1 millivolt, full audio

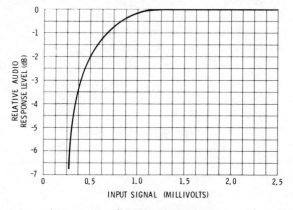

Fig. 5-15. Limiting characteristic of RCA integrated circuit used at 10.7 MHz for i-f and limiting purposes.

recovery (which is the same as saying full limiting) takes place. Since the IC can be designed in circuit to provide a voltage gain of about 60 dB, an input of only 1 *microvolt* applied to the first of two cascaded IC stages could, in theory, result in full limiting! In practice some other losses occur, but it is easy to see that no more than two such high-gain limiting circuits would generally be enough for a complete fm i-f design right up to the discriminator. Some of the newest IC's even include the few parts necessary for fm detection as well, so that we are beginning to see complete i-f systems consisting of nothing more than a couple of IC's, a couple of crystal filters or other frequency-sensitive devices, and a few necessary surrounding capacitors which cannot be included because of their large size.

To the reader who has patiently been following these megahertz signals the past five chapters—take heart! We shall now begin to explore the various methods available for converting that wandering 10.7 MHz into meaningful audio information at last.

Chapter 6

FM Detectors

THE DISCRIMINATOR
AS AN FM DETECTOR

Having followed the fm signal through its conversion to an i-f of 10.7 MHz and its subsequent amplification and limiting, we now have to remove the audio information from its i-f carrier. This process is known as fm detection or demodulation. The two most popular circuits used for this vital function remain basically unchanged. They are the so-called Foster-Seeley discriminator and the ratio detector. We shall first examine the discriminator.

Fig. 6-1 is a schematic of an early form of discriminator and, although it is not in use today, it is simpler to understand than the later-developed Foster-Seeley type. L1 and C1 form the output load of the preceding final limiter stage. This tuned circuit is broad enough to pass the 200 kHz (or more) bandwidth deemed necessary in fm reception. L1-C1 energy is inductively coupled to two secondary tuned circuits, L2-C2 and L3-C3. To obtain fm detection, L2-C2 is tuned to a frequency about 100 kHz below the i-f (10.7 MHz), while L3-C3 is tuned above the i-f center point by an equal number of kHz. Fig. 2 is a combined plot of the response curves of the two adjacent resonant circuits. Note that the L3-C3 response curve is inverted with respect to the L2-C2 curve, indicating an inverted polarity conforming with the actual hook-up and polarities established in Fig. 6-1. Thus, if the voltage appearing across R1 is larger than the voltage across R2, the net output voltage (with reference to ground) will be positive. A negative resultant output voltage will result if the voltage across R2 is greater than the voltage across R1. It should be noted that each of these resonant circuits may be looked upon as a complete a-m detector, including its own diode rectifier, load resistor, and even rf bypass capacitors (C4 and C5).

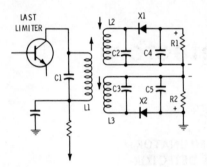

Fig. 6-1. An early version of a discriminator or fm detector.

Since each of the resonant circuits is tuned to a different frequency, the amplitude developed across their respective loads will differ, depending upon the instantaneous frequency present. With no modulation present (frequency dormant at 10.7 MHz), equal, small positive and negative voltages will be developed across R1 and R2, respectively. Being opposite in polarity, these voltages will cancel each other out and the resultant will be zero, as it should be for a "no-modulation" condition.

Suppose now that the instantaneous frequency shifts to point "A" as a result of some instantaneous modulation. The voltage across L3-C3 will be greater than that across L2-C2 because the frequency is closer to the resonant point of the L3-C3 circuit. As seen in Fig. 6-2, the instantaneous resultant voltage developed across the combination load of R1 and R2 will be negative. Furthermore, as the frequency of the carrier (and hence the i-f stages) shifts back and forth at a rate determined by the audio tone to be reproduced, the output across this combination load will rise and fall through positive and negative values, effectively converting frequency variations into their corresponding amplitude or audio variations.

Since the output voltage is really the difference in voltage across R1 and R2, both curves can be represented as one continuous curve, as shown in Fig. 6-3. This is the familiar "S" curve so often referred to in alignment instructions for fm sets. The central, linear portion of the curve must be at least 150 kHz from point 1 to point 2 if distortion-free audio demodulation is to take place. Generally, 250 kHz and even more of linear region is designed into these circuits to insure against slight mistuning away from center of channel and to further reduce audio distortion.

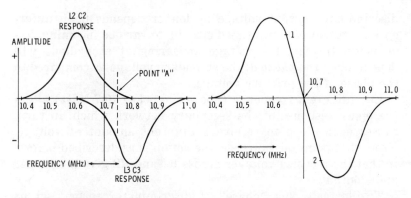

Fig. 6-2. Superimposed response curves for the secondary tuned circuits of Fig. 6-1.

Fig. 6-3. Combined "S" curve of the discriminator shows linear portion from point 1 to point 2.

To summarize the action of this early form of discriminator, it may be said that two separate actions occur. First, the tuned sections convert frequency modulation to amplitude modulation at intermediate frequencies. Then, by inserting a diode detector, the audio-modulated intermediate frequencies are converted to the desired audio. From the foregoing, you can deduce that this form of discriminator is sensitive to a-m variations, and it is for this reason that limiters must be used ahead of the discriminator, so that the discriminator input is "pure" fm with no a-m content.

From the foregoing simple analysis we go on to the Foster-Seeley, shown in one of its many forms in Fig. 6-4. In this circuit, both secondary windings are combined and a single capacitor is used to tune the circuit to 10.7 MHz. Inductive tuning of both primary and secondary is usually employed. The

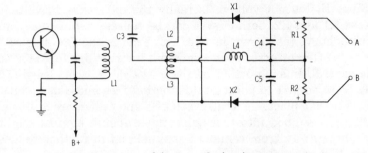

Fig. 6-4. One version of the Foster-Seeley discriminator circuit.

discriminator output voltage no longer depends upon difference in response of two tuned circuits to various incoming frequencies. Instead, the voltage appearing at each diode will depend upon the *phase* of the secondary voltage as compared to the phase of the primary voltage.

Each different frequency (above and below 10.7 MHz) alters the phase response of the secondary network which, in turn, causes each diode to receive a different amount of voltage. From that point on, however, the action is as described before, in that the rectified voltages across R1 and R2 give the proper audio output.

To illustrate this "phase" of discriminator theory, let us consider what happens first when the incoming i-f signal is at its mid-point (10.7 MHz) or with no modulation applied. The voltage induced in the secondary E_{in} produces an in-phase secondary current, I_s, since, at resonance the impedance presented is purely resistive.

On the vector diagram of Fig. 6-5, E_{in} and I_s are therefore drawn along the same straight line. The voltage developed in L_2 and L_3 due to I_s is 90 degrees out of phase with I_s. This, of course, is true of any inductance. In the vector diagram, E_2 and E_3 (the voltages developed across L_2 and L_3) are both drawn at 90 degrees from I_s. These two voltage vectors are drawn on

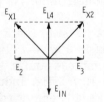

Fig. 6-5. Vector relationships in the discriminator of Fig. 6-4 with no demodulation. Voltages E_{V1} (across R1) and E_{V2} (across R2) cause currents that cancel each other.

opposite sides of I_s because of the reference center tap on the secondary coil. With reference to this center tap, E_2 and E_3 are 180 degrees out of phase with each other. Now, if E_{L4} (the equivalent primary voltage which can be shown to appear across L_4) is added vectorially to E_2 we obtain E_{v1}. By adding E_{L4} to E_3 we also obtain E_{v2}, the two respective voltages applied to the diodes V1 and V2. It is obvious from the diagram that E_{v1} and E_{v2} are exactly equal in amplitude. Therefore there will be the same current through each diode, and similar voltages will appear across R_1 and R_2. Being out of phase, these voltages will cancel and there will be no audio output. Again, this is as it should be, since no modulation is applied to the signal, which remains static at 10.7 MHz.

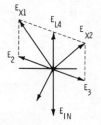

Fig. 6-6. Phase relationships when frequency is shifted above resonance cause E_{v1} to be greater than E_{v2}, and a net output voltage (+) will appear across R1 and R2.

By way of contrast, let us consider the case in which the fm signal, now modulated, swings towards a higher frequency. As shown in Fig. 6-6, E_{in} and E_{L4} still bear the same reference relationhsip to each other (namely, 180 degrees apart in phase). At frequencies above resonance, however, X_L (the inductive reactance) exceeds X_c (capacitive reactance) and the current, I_s, will lag behind E_{in}. E_2 and E_3 still maintain a 90-degree relationship to I_s, however, since that relationship always exists between the voltage and the current in a given coil. If we once again add E_2 to E_{L4} and E_3 to E_{L4}, vectorially, we see that resultant E_{v1} is now greater than resultant E_{v2}. As a result, the voltage developed across R_1 will be greater than that developed across R2, and the output voltage will be positive with respect to ground or the center tap.

A similar, but opposite phase analysis by means of another vector diagram could easily be drawn for the case in which the incoming frequency shifts below center, in which case the output voltage would be negative with respect to ground. The unbalanced condition that arises from the shifting frequency (either negative or positive) is made linear with respect to frequency by careful design of the discriminator transformer so that the audio output will be a faithful replica of the audio which caused the modulation at the transmitter. The S curve previously shown applies equally to this design; the linear portion can be made just as great as in the previous case.

A modification of the Foster-Seeley circuit is shown in Fig. 6-7. At first glance you might suppose that voltage E_{L4}, the reference voltage needed for proper operation of the discriminator, has been eliminated with the removal of L4. Actually, however, R2 is now effectively in parallel with L1 (thanks to coupling capacitor C3) ; therefore E_1 appears across R_2. In this

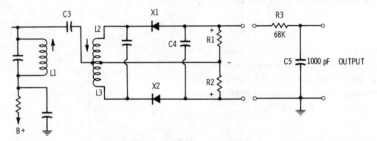

Fig. 6-7. Modified version of a discriminator, in which L4 and C5 have been omitted, also shows parts needed for proper de-emphasis.

circuit, R2 performs a double function—it develops the rectified voltage from the diode and serves to apply E_1, the reference voltage, to the opposite diode. The advantage of this configuration lies only in the fact that fewer parts are required. R1 and R2 must be high in value, however, because they are effectively in parallel with L1. In the original Foster-Seeley circuit (Fig. 6-4), L4 served as a choke, isolating R1 and R2 from L1. For reasons which we shall go into when we discuss stereo fm, the higher output impedance can sometimes create problems in coupling to a stereo fm decoder.

Whether a discriminator or a ratio detector is used in a given design, there remains one important job to be done before the demodulated audio can be applied to an audio amplifier. You will recall that the frequency response of the program material broadcast is anything but flat in the high-fidelity sense. Rather, the high frequencies above about 1500 Hz have been deliberately boosted to improve the signal-to-noise ratio of the overall received signal. The scheme is called "pre-emphasis." In order to restore flat response, a de-emphasis network must now be introduced. R3 and C5 in Fig. 6-7 serve this function. Note that the RC time constant, as shown, is only 68 microseconds, as opposed to 75 microseconds used at the transmitting end. Usually, length of connecting shielded cable and/or stray wiring capacity make up the difference. Sometimes, less meticulous designers will *under*-de-emphasize recovered audio in order to create a more "brilliant" sounding output, but they are only deluding themselves and the public. Further, this causes inaccurate frequency response and a less-than-optimum signal-to-noise condition.

THE RATIO DETECTOR

The conventional form of fm detector, the Foster-Seeley discriminator, is sensitive to a-m variations as well as to desired fm deviation or modulation. As a result, one or more limiter stages is required to remove all amplitude modulation and apply a pure fm signal to the input of the discriminator.

In the mid-1940's, a circuit was developed that was sensitive to frequency variations, though much less sensitive to amplitude variations. This circuit, dubbed the ratio-detector, may therefore be thought of as a combination limiter-detector. In widespread use today, the ratio detector, as used in high-quality tuner designs, is still preceded by one or more limiters. But this is done to afford even more a-m rejection than would be possible if the same amount of limiting circuitry preceded a conventional discriminator.

In order to understand the limiting action of a ratio detector, let us refer to Fig. 6-8, which is the schematic of the Foster-Seeley discriminator that appeared in identical form in foregoing paragraphs. As shown then, equal voltages appear across R1 and R2 when the incoming i-f signal is centered at 10.7 MHz (no audio information being transmitted). Assume that with a certain carrier strength and a given modulation the voltage across R1 increases from a quiescent value of 3 volts to 4 volts, and that the voltage across R2 decreases from its static value of 3 volts to 2 volts. The net output voltage (instantaneous) would be the difference, or 2 volts. Now assume a stronger incoming i-f signal, arising from a stronger carrier signal so

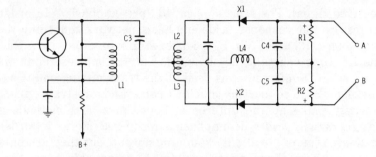

Fig. 6-8. Schematic of the Foster-Seeley discriminator.

that the voltage across R1 and R2 is now 6 volts instead of 3 volts. With the same modulation applied as before, but with this stronger carrier, the voltage across R1 will rise to 8 volts while the voltage across R2 will decrease to 4 volts, a net difference (and instantaneous output) of 4 volts.

Despite the fact that the same modulation has been applied in both cases, the amplitude of output in the second case is twice as large as in the case of the weaker incoming rf signal. This amounts to direct a-m response as well as fm response and is the reason why limiting is needed with the discriminator circuit. There is, however, an interesting numerical relationship between the two examples cited. The ratio of voltages across R1 and R2 in the first example—4/2—exactly equals the ratio of voltages across these resistors in the second example—8/4. It is this equality of voltage ratios, regardless of incoming signal strength, that gives rise to the idea of the ratio detector.

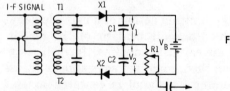

Fig. 6-9. Explanatory form of a ratio detector.

The concept of ratio detector operation can be best understood by examining the circuit of Fig. 6-9, in which each diode is associated with a completely separate resonant circuit. Let us again assume that the circuit involving X1 is tuned above 10.7 MHz, while that of X2 is tuned below 10.7 MHz. The output voltage for the X1 circuit will appear across C1 while the output voltage for X2 will appear across C2. The battery V_b is a fixed voltage. Since C1 and C2 in series are directly across this battery, the instantaneous sum of their voltages must equal V_b. Also note that the polarity of the battery is such that under static or no-signal conditions, no current can appear in the circuit consisting of T1, T2, X2, C2, C1, X1 and T1. Now, although E1 + E2 can never exceed or be less than V_b, E1 does not necessarily have to equal E2.

In other words, the *ratio* E1/E2 may vary! Output signal (recovered audio) can be taken from a variable load resistor connected across C2, since the voltage across this capacitor will vary with signal.

When the incoming signal is unmodulated (10.7 MHz), E1 and E2 will be equal. This is similar to the situation that prevails with the discriminators examined earlier. When the incoming signal rises in frequency because of modulation applied, it approaches the resonant frequency of T1, resulting in a higher voltage across C1. At the same time, a lower voltage is developed across T2. Therefore the voltage across C2 decreases. However, the sum of these two voltages must still equal V_b.

In other words, an instantaneous change in frequency alters the ratio of E1/E2, but not the total voltage. With a signal frequency modulated to a point below 10.7 MHz, E2 will exceed E1, but, again, the ratio of E1/E2 will remain constant because of the stabilizing effect of V_b. Desired audio information is obtained from the voltage variations across C2. Since only audio variations are desired, C3 serves to block the dc voltage present at all times across C2.

The key to this explanation is, of course, V_b, which keeps the total voltage constant while permitting the ratio of E1/E2 to vary. Thus, in this elementary circuit, an output voltage is obtained that is purely a result of the fm signal. In actual practice the use of a battery would severely limit the dynamic range of such a circuit. For example, if V_b were made very high, weak incoming signals would be lost entirely because they would not possess sufficient amplitude to overcome the negative "back bias" placed on diodes X1 and X2 by V_b. If V_b were to be made quite low, then more powerful stations would be severely limited in the amount of audio voltage that could be recovered from the circuit because the voltage across either capacitor (or even the sum of voltages across both C1 and C2) could never exceed the low value imposed by V_b.

In practical circuits, the value of V_b is not determined by a fixed battery, but by the average value of each incoming carrier. This idea will be understood better by examining Fig. 6-10, a practical form of ratio detector.

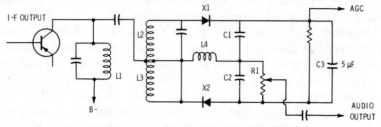

Fig. 6-10. Practical form of ratio-detector circuit.

This circuit uses the same phase-shifting properties as the discriminator of Fig. 6-8. R and C3 replace V_b, the battery, and the voltage developed across R will be dependent upon the strength of incoming signal. Notice that X1 and X2 are in series with R and all current through these diodes must go through R. By placing a 5-μF capacitor across R, a fairly constant voltage is maintained and momentary changes in signal amplitude are absorbed by this capacitor. It is only when the average value of the incoming signal changes (as when tuning from a stronger station to a weaker one) that the voltage across R changes significantly. Audio output is still taken from across C2. Since the voltage across R is dependent upon incoming signal strength, it may be used as an agc (automatic gain control) voltage. The ratio detector in this form does possess the disadvantage of being somewhat more difficult to align; also, great care must be taken to obtain a linear response characteristic both during alignment, as well as in the design of the ratio-detector transformer in the first place.

A more symmetrical form of ratio-detector design (and one that is almost always used in preference to the form just discussed) is shown in Fig. 6-11. Instead of the direct capacitive connection between L1 and the secondary tap, we now introduce L4. Using the same reasoning as was applied in our earlier discussion of discriminators, we see that the voltage induced in L4 (which is closely coupled physically to L1) will

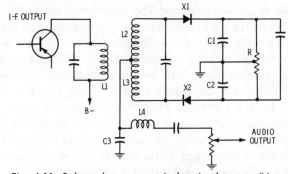

Fig. 6-11. Balanced or symmetrical ratio detector. (Note: "R" may consist of two fixed resistors in practice.)

remain constant so long as the primary voltage is constant. Since the voltage across L4 depends upon the voltage across L1, and not upon the secondary circuit, it can be used as the reference voltage in place of the previous capacitive-coupled arrangement of Fig. 6-10.

The path from the center tap of the secondary to the junction of C1 and C2 includes L4 and C3. Voltage applied to X1 consists of E_{L4} and E_{L2}, while voltage applied to X2 consists of E_{L4} and E_{L3}. At 10.7 MHz (center intermediate frequency), both diodes receive the same voltage, with C1 and C2 reaching the same potential. The current path from X2 is through L3, through L4 to C3 to ground, and thence through C2. Current continues until the voltage across C3 and C2 equals the voltage at the diode. Current from X1 is from its cathode through C1, C3, and L4 and up through L2, and back through X1 until C1 and C3 are charged to the voltage at the diode. The current path from X2 is through L4 and C3 in the opposite direction from the current produced by X1. Therefore, these two currents in the common branch (L4 and C3) actually oppose each other and the resultant voltage is zero.

At frequencies above and below 10.7 MHz, the voltage applied to each diode will vary and a net current will take place through C3 and L4. When frequency varies in one direction, a positive voltage will be developed across C3 and L4; when frequency varies in the other direction, a negative voltage will be developed. The potential variations across C3 will vary directly with frequency and, therefore, represent audio information.

Both the ratio detector and the discriminator have one advantage in common in that there is a point in each circuit at which there is a zero dc potential when the set is tuned accurately to the center of the channel. First, the popular zero-center tuning meter can be connected (with suitable impedance isolation) to this circuit point. When a station is properly tuned in, the meter pointer will rest at the center of the scale. When the station is detuned, the needle will indicate a positive or negative voltage, depending on which way the signal is detuned. This meter is the easiest to use, visually, and is often present in good-quality tuners or receivers.

Perhaps more important, the zero center feature of these circuits provides a convenient take-off point for some form of afc (automatic frequency control) used to "lock in" fm stations, once properly tuned. Without detailing these afc circuits at this time, it is obvious that a voltage that is zero when a station is properly tuned in and varies above and below zero when the station is detuned can be used to retune the receiver electronically.

To sum up the difference between the ratio detector and the discriminator, the latter operates on the difference of the output voltages of two diode detectors. Diode-load resistors are connected with their voltages in opposition. The resultant of the two voltages becomes the audio output voltage. Since the discriminator responds to amplitude modulation as well as fm, it must be preceded by one or more limiters and requires a great deal of amplification in order to drive these limiters into saturation. Ordinarily, this requirement makes for a more costly design.

In the ratio-detector circuit, the two diodes are connected in series and a stabilizing or controlling voltage is developed that depends upon the strength of the incoming carrier signal. The controlling voltage sets the limit of maximum audio voltage that can be obtained. The ratio detector is more immune to a-m variations than the Foster-Seeley discriminator (considered without limiter), and it is generally more economical since it requires fewer amplification stages ahead of it. Often, a limiter, or an i-f stage acting as a partial limiter, will precede a ratio detector to improve a-m rejection further. As a consequence of the foregoing, most "hi-fi" tuners today employ a ratio detector.

MORE ON FM DETECTION

Having examined the two most popularly used forms of fm demodulators (discriminator and ratio detector), we must not overlook two more recent forms of fm detection circuits that have had some acceptance. These are the "gated beam" detector and the "counter" detector.

In its earliest forms, the gated-beam detector utilized a specially constructed tube, the 6BN6. When grid voltage values changed from negative to positive, plate current of this tube rose rapidly from zero to some predetermined maximum value, which remained constant regardless of how positive the grid voltage became. Current cut-off was abruptly achieved when grid voltage reached a negative value of 2 volts. Later, simpler forms (structurally) of tubes were developed that resembled pentodes physically, but which still exhibited sharp current turn-on and turn-off characteristics.

Perhaps the most popular of these is the 6DT6, and we shall use this tube type to demonstrate the action of a gated-beam fm detector. Fig. 6-12 will help to illustrate the operation of this circuit.

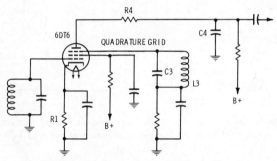

Fig. 6-12. Partial circuit of gated-beam fm detector.

R1 serves to apply 1 or 2 volts of cathode bias to the tube. Under such conditions of bias, incoming 10.7-MHz signals need not have much amplitude to cut off current during negative half cycles of the signal. Similarly, for positive halves of the signal cycle, tube saturation is reached. In this way, the tube acts as an effective limiter, clipping any a-m components from the incoming signal. The grid construction is such that current is released and ended suddenly. Therefore, tube current appears in the plate circuit in the form of pulses. The screen grid (sometimes called the accelerator grid, in this circuit) has a positive voltage applied to it which accelerates the electron stream and increases its velocity.

The upper grid (known as the quadrature grid), instead of being bypassed to cathode or ground (as would be the case in a conventional pentode hookup), is connected to a parallel-resonant circuit consisting of L3 and C3. These components are chosen to be resonant at the 10.7-MHz incoming intermediate frequency. During periods of conduction, pulses apply bursts of energy to the quadrature resonant circuit and, because of the Q of this circuit, sinusoidal signals are developed across the resonant circuit. Construction of the tube and the nature of the coupling to this grid cause this quadrature signal to lag the input signal by 90 degrees.

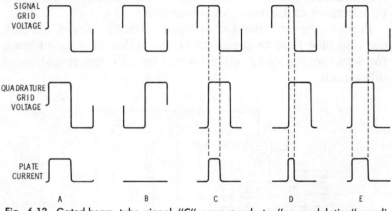

Fig. 6-13. Gated-beam tube signal "C" corresponds to "no modulation" condition, while signals "D" and "E" represent deviation above and below 10.7 MHz respectively.

Since either the signal grid or the quadrature grid can influence current flow in this tube, either grid can cause cutoff of current when it has a sufficiently negative voltage applied to it. At shown in Fig. 6-13A, when both the input and the quadrature grid have positive voltages, in phase, current lasts for a full half cycle. If the two grids ever have voltages which are 180 degrees out of phase, there will be no current (as in Fig. 6-13B). In Fig. 6-13C we see the condition described above—voltage on the quadrature grid is 90 degrees behind incoming signal grid voltage and the resulting pulse-width of plate current is only half as great as in Fig. 6-13A, or one-quarter of a cycle in duration.

As the incoming signal is frequency-modulated, the carrier frequency (applied to the first signal grid) shifts above and below its center. This frequency variation also alters the situation with respect to the quadrature grid voltage. As the incoming signal shifts to a higher frequency, the resonant circuit C3-L3 (Fig. 6-12) becomes capacitive and the signal voltage lags the input signal voltage by more than 90 degrees, as illustrated in Fig. 6-13D. Under these conditions the current pulses that appear in the plate circuit become narrower. Conversely, as the incoming signal becomes lower in frequency, the quadrature resonant circuit begins to look inductive and the voltage lag is less than 90 degrees. The result is an increase in plate current pulse width, as shown in Fig. 6-13E. As the carrier shifts above and below the 10.7 MHz center frequency in accordance with desired audio modulation, a series of pulses of different widths is developed in the plate circuit. The full series for a single alternation of sine-wave is shown in Fig. 6-14A.

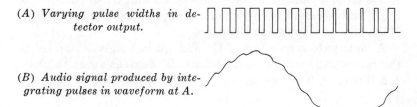

(A) *Varying pulse widths in detector output.*

(B) *Audio signal produced by integrating pulses in waveform at A.*

Fig. 6-14. Action of gated-beam detector.

At this point, the "counting" or integrating circuit consisting of R4 and C4 (Fig. 6-12), acts upon the square-wave output pulses. In effect, it "averages out" the dc value of the pulse train, as shown in Fig. 6-14B. This "ragged-edged" waveform corresponds exactly to the desired audio signal. While further filtering can be used to remove the sawtooth edge of the waveform, even if it were applied to an audio amplifier without change you would hear only the desired audio because its fundamental repetition rate of 10.7 MHz would be inaudible. Usually the de-emphasis circuit required to restore

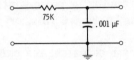

correct frequency response, as shown in Fig. 6-15, will remove
any remaining 10.7 MHz because the required time constant
is 75 microseconds.

SOLID-STATE CIRCUITRY

You may recall that the audio information, as applied to
the transmitter modulating circuits of the transmitter, was
deliberately *pre-emphasized* to improve signal-to-noise ratios
and now, regardless of what type of fm detector is used, corresponding *de-emphasis* must be inserted following demodulation.

Translated to solid-state circuitry, a simplified form of
gate-quadrature type of demodulator is shown in Fig. 6-16.
This circuit is similar to the one used in connection with a
demodulator for SCA (Background Music) fm transmission.
Aside from a change in the values of L1 and C1 to conform to
the Q and resonant requirements of an incoming signal of 10.7
MHz, the principles are the same.

A logic gate consisting of Q1 and Q2 has signals applied to
the respective base inputs which are 90 degrees apart in phase
(in this case, a series resonant circuit is used, and voltage to

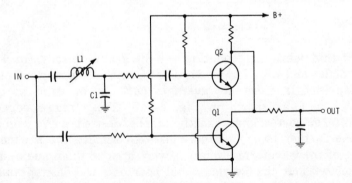

Fig. 6-16. Two transistors arranged in a "gate" circuit for fm demodulation. The
combination of L1 and C1 produces a phase shift of signal applied to Q2.

the lower input is taken at the junction of L1 and C1 to effect the 90-degree phase shift). Conduction through the gate takes place only when both cases are positive, and this period will vary as the modulated i-f signal varies above and below the center value of 10.7 MHz. Unlike the gated-beam tube arrangement, however, limiting must precede the gate circuit so that a pair of "clipped" or square waveforms are presented to the two inputs of the gate. Once again, the output pulses are integrated by an RC circuit of suitable time constant, and normal de-emphasis is applied after integration.

The two circuits described, while discussed as "counting" circuits, have an advantage over the so-called pure counter-detector. In the latter circuit, the incoming signal is first fully limited, as usual. Conduction may be further limited by differentiating the pulses so that they are very narrow spikes. As the incoming frequency is lowered, because of modulation, the pulses will be further apart; with increasing frequency, the pulses will be closer together. By applying these pulses to another stage of amplification, followed by an integrating or counter circuit, the instantaneous dc value of the pulses is averaged; this average represents the wave shape of the desired audio information.

With a center frequency of 10.7 MHz and a maximum possible deviation of only 75 kHz above and below this center value, you can readily see that the difference in spacing between pulses, even at the two extremes, will be very small, relatively speaking. It is for this reason that this form of detector, while extremely linear, recovers very little audio output and is usually followed by one or more audio amplification stages. While these stages increase the level of audio, they do not materially improve the inherent signal-to-noise ratio of the system. For this reason, the "pure" counter detector is now seldom used in commercial fm circuitry.

If one had to rate the detectors discussed in terms of popularity, it would run about like this: The discriminator, once the most popular form of fm demodulator, now rates in second place, and a low second place at that. Some of its recent disfavor stems from the ratio detector's inherently lower cost and less-stringent limiting requirements ahead of it in the circuit. A less apparent reason is the comparatively lower output impedance associated with the more popular ratio-detector circuits. A low output impedance means that capacitive loading associated with shielded output cables (in the case of tuners only) will not adversely affect frequency response. Further, in the case of stereo fm, it is necessary to recover frequencies (audio) all the way up to 53 kHz for application to the stereo fm decoder circuits that follow. Even a small amount of stray capacitance across the output of a high-impedance discriminator might attenuate the higher frequencies involved. Finally, since solid-state circuitry has become so popular, the output of a ratio detector, being low impedance in nature, is most easily applied to the audio amplifier input stages that normally follow, without the necessity of having extra stages of impedance matching circuitry.

The demodulation circuits examined at the conclusion of this chapter are not used nearly as often as the ratio detector or even the Foster-Seeley discriminator (at least in the field of broadcast fm). The gated-beam tube is often found in TV sets, however, where the sound portion of the signal is frequency modulated. In this application, the high sensitivity of this form of detection (high audio recovery) is particularly attractive, since, as we all know, *sound* is deemed to be relatively unimportant by TV manufacturers.

Chapter 7

Circuit
Refinements for FM

AUTOMATIC FREQUENCY CONTROL

The need for accurate center-of-channel tuning in fm reception (and even more so in stereo fm reception) has been stressed in earlier chapters. Consider, for a moment, what takes place in a relatively narrow-band i-f system if the listener is tuned as little as 50 kHz off-center from optimum frequency. Fig. 7-1 shows a discriminator or ratio detector "S" curve, in which the perfectly linear portion extends about 90 kHz to either side of 10.7 MHz—more than the 75 kHz minimum required, but not very much more. Point A on the curve represents center-of-channel tuning, while point B represents a point 50 kHz too high, or off-center, to which the unsuspecting listener has tuned. So long as the program being transmitted is relatively low in audio level (quiet music passages, etc.), this amount of de-tuning will cause no audible defects in the received signal. Suppose, however, that a loud passage of music comes along which causes a full, or almost full ±75 kHz deviation of the main carrier (and therefore, the same amount of deviation of the 10.7 MHz i-f signal). Every time the carrier is shifted upward in frequency, the last 35 kHz or

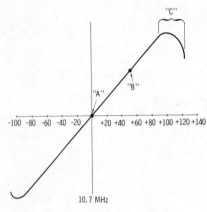

Fig. 7-1. Detector response showing linear portion centered about 10.7 MHz (point A).

so of deviation will encounter a very nonlinear portion of the detector S curve, designated by the bracketed length C in Fig. 7-1. Instead of being perfectly sinusoidal, the resultant recovered audio will appear as shown in Fig. 7-2—severely distorted at one extreme of its excursion. As illustrated in the figure, this amounts to about 20 percent or more of distortion and would be most unpleasant to listen to.

Assuming that the average listener cannot be expected to always tune to exact center-of-channel (in the absence of any visual indicator to tell him when the set is properly tuned), there are only two solutions to this problem. The first is to make the i-f and detector bandwidth so great (say, 300 or 400 kHz for the linear portion of the S curve), that even when a station is carelessly tuned in, there is likely to be at least 75 kHz of linear detection curve on either side of the tuned point. However, no matter how wide the linear portion of the detector characteristic is, there will still be those listeners who might tune close to one end of that linear portion, with the same disastrous results, as depicted in Fig. 7-2. The second, more common solution is to incorporate a sensing cir-

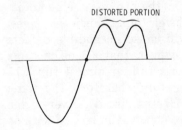

Fig. 7-2. Distorted audio sine wave caused by detuning narrow-band i-f system to point B in Fig. 7-1.

cuit which detects errors in tuning and automatically corrects for them. Such a circuit is called automatic frequency control, usually abbreviated afc.

You may recall that in an earlier discussion of fm broadcasting techniques, we discussed the function of a reactance tube modulator. This was a tube (or transistor) circuit which was effectively placed across the basic rf oscillator in such a way that it appeared as an additional inductance or capacitance in parallel with the frequency-determining elements of the main oscillator. As varying audio was applied to this circuit, its effective contribution of "L" or "C" varied accordingly, causing the master oscillator to shift back and forth in frequency. Had we applied fixed values of dc potential to this circuit instead of audio, we could have shifted the oscillator frequency as well, for the audio information applied might really be thought of as continuously varying instantaneous dc levels.

Now, every fm tuner or receiver contains a local oscillator whose selected frequency determines which incoming rf signal will beat with it to produce the desired 10.7-MHz signal for application to the i-f and detector stages that follow. Alter the local-oscillator frequency and you alter the signal frequency which, when subtracted from the oscillator frequency, results in 10.7 MHz.

Both the ratio detector and the Foster-Seeley discriminator are ideally suited for providing a necessary dc correcting voltage to apply to a circuit such as a reactance tube. The audio take-off point produces 0 volts of dc when the incoming frequency is exactly 10.7 MHz and also produces positive or negative voltages when that frequency is above or below 10.7 MHz. Fig. 7-3 illustrates an early tube-type local-oscillator circuit together with a second triode section used as a reactance tube in parallel with the tuned circuit. The voltage applied to pin 7 of this triode is derived (after suitable bypassing to eliminate audio variations) from the output of the fm detector (not shown). Polarities of the various voltages have to work in a prescribed manner for afc correction. For example, suppose that when a station is detuned on the high side of correct frequency a positive voltage appears at the detector output. If the reactance tube appears to be inductive, the application of this positive voltage to the grid of the reactance tube must have the effect of *increasing* the effective inductance contributed by the reactance circuit. An increase in total inductance will result in a *decrease* in local-oscillator frequency and so the effect is to bring the tuner closer to correct tuning. Of course, this form of afc can never bring the tuned frequency exactly to center, for the corrective action depends upon the presence of some error voltage and if the tuner were perfectly tuned, there would be no error voltage appearing at the output of the detector. Properly designed afc circuits can, however, reduce the tuning error to 1/5th of its original value. Thus, detuning of a station by 50 kHz (as in our first example) can be reduced to about 10 kHz, which is quite insignificant.

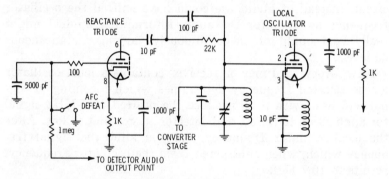

Fig. 7-3. Early afc circuit using reactance tube principle.

Many tuners and receivers have two selector-switch positions for fm tuning. In the first position, the afc circuits are defeated by shorting the dc correcting voltage to ground. With no variable dc applied to the grid of the reactance tube, this tube then represents a fixed inductance under all conditions and does not act to correct tuning errors. This feature enables the user to tune in the station as best he can first without afc. Then, the selector switch is thrown to the FM-AFC position to correct for any remaining error and to lock the station in. This phrase, "locking the station in," has given rise to a very great misconception about afc. Many users have been led to believe (through implied advertising claims), that afc is a cure-all for tuner drift problems. Nothing could be further from the truth. If a local oscillator is improperly designed so that it drifts for long periods after turn-on because of a change in temperature, a change in power-supply voltage (caused by fluctuating power-line voltage levels), or from other causes, afc can do nothing to prevent such drift problems. In fact, in a certain sense, afc makes the condition worse. The user may *think* that he is properly tuned to a station because the afc circuits have reduced the real tuning error from, say, 50 kHz to 10 kHz. As the improperly designed local oscillator begins to drift further, in the same direction as the original error, for example, the afc circuits cannot keep "pulling" the oscillator back towards center indefinitely. A point is reached where the dc correcting voltage, instead of becoming greater and greater, drops to zero once more (as the extreme end of the detector S curve response is reached), and the station "pops out of lock" all at once, instead of gradually, as would be the case if no afc were applied.

The rapidly expanding use of solid-state circuitry in fm design has given rise to a new form of afc circuit. It was long ago discovered that a simple diode, biased to a state of nonconduction, appears to be capacitive. Further, diodes can be so constructed that their apparent capacitance can be made to vary quite linearly with a change in reverse bias voltage. Obviously, such diodes lend themselves very readily to afc circuits, replacing the more complex reactance-tube circuitry. A late model, transistorized, fm local-oscillator circuit is shown in Fig. 7-4. Here, X1 is a voltage-tuned capacitive diode that forms a frequency-determining element of the oscillator

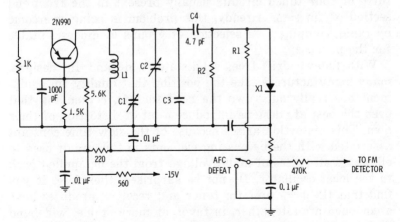

Fig. 7-4. Modern afc circuit used with transistorized local oscillator.

resonant circuit in much the same way as do L1, C1, C2, and C3. Back bias is applied through a voltage divider consisting of R1 and R2. C4 is in series with the capacitive-looking diode so that the capacitive changes brought about by various values of corrective dc applied at the anode end of the diode will not cause too great a frequency shift. In every other respect, the circuit behaves in the same manner as that shown earlier, in Fig. 7-3. Before leaving the subject of voltage-tunable diodes, it may have occurred to you that if a diode can be made to look like a variable capacitor by applying varying values of dc to it, then such a diode (or several of them) might well be used to replace the multisection, bulky, variable capacitor used in most fm front ends to tune in stations across the entire 88-108 MHz fm band. The fact is that many such designs are already appearing on the market. The tuning control for such sets need only be a simple potentiometer which picks off a desired voltage to "tune" the diode-capacitance to desired values. Such designs lend themselves particularly well to push-button operated fm sets. In such sets, the push buttons, instead of being coupled to a complex mechanism that rotates the variable capacitor to a preselected setting, need only pick off a preselected voltage to apply to the diodes that replace this variable capacitor.

While this would seem to be an ideal new scheme for tuning fm radios, thus far it has found limited use because of the difficulty in matching up perfectly tracking diodes for the three or four tuned circuits usually present in the front-end section of fm sets. Already, this problem is being overcome by rapid, computerized selection of groups of diodes suitable for the purpose.

With today's drift-free, solid-state, wideband fm designs, many manufacturers take the position that quality fm equipment has really outgrown the need for afc, contending that even the best afc designs introduce a bit of distortion of their own. This distortion arises because of the slow time constant associated with the by-passing elements in the circuit used to eliminate all traces of audio voltage from the dc applied back to the local oscillator. Do not be surprised, therefore, if you find that the *very best* fm tuner and receiver products have abandoned afc altogether, in favor of more stable, wideband designs. How, then, are you expected to tune such a set to exact center of channel? By means of the tuning meters and other visual aids that we shall discuss next.

TUNING AIDS IN FM RECEIVERS

With the trend in fm receiver design tending to veer away from afc circuitry (at least in the more expensive fm units), a visual tuning aid to assist the user in proper, exact center-of-channel tuning has become increasingly important. There are three devices used to provide a visual indication of correct tuning—the old "tuning eye" or vacuum tube containing a fluorescent target, the tuning meter and the small cathode-ray tube (similar to those used in oscilloscopes). Tuning eyes and tuning meters have been used in fm tuners and receivers for over two decades. The use of a cathode-ray tube as a tuning indicator is a much more recent innovation and one which, to date, will be found only in very expensive equipment, since it entails the addition of a considerable amount of extra circuitry just to activate the cathode-ray tube.

Tuning Eyes

The first popularly used tuning eye tube was the 6E5. This tube, like many of its later variations, contained a triode section which functioned as a dc amplifier whose plate was directly coupled to a rod, known as the ray-control electrode, which, in turn, governed the flow of electrons to the fluorescent screen. A schematic representation of such a device is shown in Fig. 7-5. With positive or slightly negative voltage applied

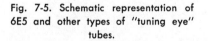
Fig. 7-5. Schematic representation of 6E5 and other types of "tuning eye" tubes.

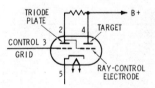

to the control grid, a large shadow area will be present on the visible face of the tube, as shown in Fig. 7-6A. As negative voltage is applied to the grid, the shadow width will decrease (Fig. 7-6B) and, if a sufficiently large negative dc voltage is applied to the grid, the shadow area will disappear completely, and an actual overlap of fluorescence will occur, as in

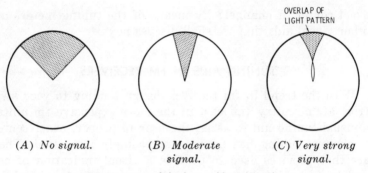

(A) No signal.   (B) Moderate   (C) Very strong
                          signal.   signal.

Fig. 7-6. Variation of shadow width in 6E5 tube.

Fig. 7-6C. Fig. 7-7 shows a partial schematic of the final limiter of a typical fm tuner and indicates how connection of this tube may be made. Since the voltage at the grid of the limiter is negative (grid-leak action) and proportional to incoming signal strength, it is of a suitable polarity to be fed directly to the grid of the 6E5 tube. In actual use, the listener would tune to a desired station and adjust the setting for maximum fluorescent area (or, minimum "shadow"). With weak stations, the shadow area will be greater than when tuning in stronger stations, but in either case a null will occur, indicating correct point of tuning.

Other forms of tuning eyes are illustrated in Fig. 7-8. The "bar" type, shown in Fig. 7-8A, operates on essentially the same principle as the 6E5, except that the fluorescent area is now a set of fluorescent bars that move closer together as

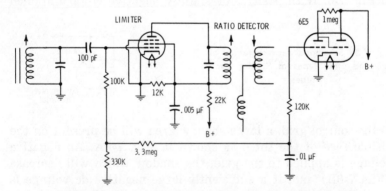

Fig. 7-7. Partial schematic showing connection of 6E5 indicator tube to final limiter circuit.

negative voltage is applied to the control grid. Visually, this form of tuning indicator is a bit easier to use since center-of-channel indication is very precise and well defined. As the vacuum-tube era in fm drew to a close, in the late 1950's and early 1960's, a very clever ultra-miniature tuning indicator, known as the DM-70 was developed and extensively used. Operating with a filament voltage of only 1.4 volts and a B+ requirement of about 90 volts or so, this sub-miniature tube had a fluorescent pattern shaped in the form of a variable "exclamation point" as shown in Fig. 7-8B. So small was this little indicator tube that many manufacturers used it as a travelling dial pointer and tuning indicator combined.

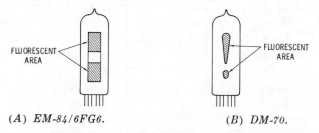

(A) EM-84/6FG6.   (B) DM-70.

Fig. 7-8. Two examples of "tuning eye" tubes.

Tuning Meters

Fluorescent indicator tubes and tuning meters co-existed for many years. The ascendancy of the tuning meter in recent years is due largely to the almost universal transition to solid-state or transistorized circuitry. Power-supply voltages in solid-state equipment (even in powerful all-in-one receivers) seldom exceed fifty to seventy-five volts dc—not enough for use as target and plate voltages with any of the fluorescent indicator tubes. Meters, on the other hand, are strictly current devices—very *low* current, at that. It is not difficult to design a small meter with a full-scale sensitivity of 100 or even 50 microamperes. A circuit using such a meter as a signal strength indicator is shown in Fig. 7-9. Note, that once again the limiter input serves as the "take-off" point, but this time, since we are dealing with a transistor stage, no grid-leak voltage is involved. Instead, a small rf coupling capacitor (2.2 pF) feeds some of the 10.7 MHz i-f voltage to a diode rectifier. The resultant dc voltage is fed directly to the meter movement, after suitable voltage-divider action. As in the previous case, this meter is a peak signal indicator, reading higher up-scale for greater signal strengths. There is one disadvantage to this type of indication. As you can see in Fig. 7-10, the i-f voltage amplitude in wideband i-f systems remains at its peak value over a rather large frequency range. As a result, a meter connected in this manner will rise to a peak reading as station frequency is approached and remain there over a rather large span of dial-pointer movement (par-

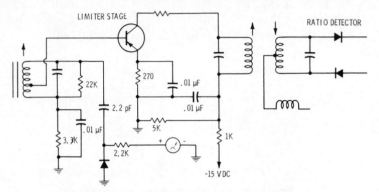

Fig. 7-9. Schematic of solid-state receiver using tuning meter connected to limiter stage.

ticularly if the incoming signal is a strong one). It is rather difficult, under these conditions, to determine where exact center of channel really is. Tuning to a center point of the "highest-reading" area is no easier than tuning to the center of "best sound", which can be done with no meter present in the first place. For this reason, many manufacturers prefer the use of a center-reading or center-zero meter. Such meters are identical to the other types, except that with no voltage applied, the pointer comes to rest at the exact center of the meter scale. With positive voltage applied, the meter pointer

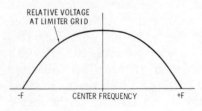

Fig. 7-10. Typical limiter grid-voltage curve in a wideband limiter shows difficulty of finding a "maximum" for tuning-meter use.

will swing to the right and with negative voltage it will swing to the left, or vice versa, depending upon circuitry.

Such positive- and negative-swinging voltage is, of course, readily available at the output of the fm detector (either a discriminator or a ratio detector) and, in a properly aligned set, is the best indicator of center-of-channel tuning. That is, zero volts dc at the audio take-off point of either a ratio-detector or a Foster-Seeley discriminator means that the set is perfectly tuned to center of channel. (It can also mean that there is no station at that point on the dial *altogether*, but that is certainly no problem for the listener.) In Fig. 7-11 such a zero-counter meter is shown connected at the output of a con-

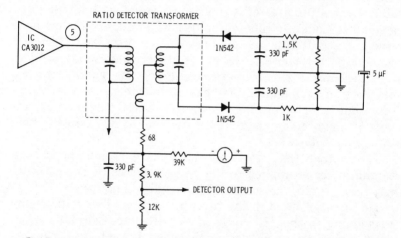

Fig. 7-11. Ratio detector stage of modern receiver showing zero-center meter connected for center-of-channel tuning indication.

ventional ratio-detector circuit. All that is needed is one resistor for dropping the voltage swings to correct value, based on the sensitivity of the meter movement. The action of the meter is such that when tuning approaches a station signal, the meter pointer will first swing sharply to one extreme or the other (depending upon whether the tuning is going up or down in frequency). As the tuning knob is tuned further, the meter pointer follows the familiar "S" curve of the detector, first approaching zero and then, if the center is inadvertently passed, swinging off in the other direction. The user can, therefore, literally "zero in" on center of channel. The indication is positive and precise and there is no guesswork about it. On the other hand, this form of meter can tell you nothing about relative signal strength of a given signal, since *all* stations, whether weakly or strongly received, will cause the meter to read zero when they are properly tuned-in. The signal-strength type of meter discussed before has the advantage of serving as an aid in orienting your receiving antenna. All you have to do with that type is to have someone rotate the antenna while you observe the meter reading for highest indication, when tuned to your desired station.

Cathode-Ray Tube Indicators

Combining the best of both types of meter indicators and adding some features of its own not present with either type, a small cathode-ray tube (usually 1 in. in diameter) has been incorporated in the design of some recently manufactured tuners and receivers. At least one other manufacturer, reluctant perhaps to penalize less demanding customers with the high cost of such an addition, has made external provisions on some units for connection to the horizontal and vertical inputs of any oscilloscope that the user might have. Here's how the 'scope tube works.

The voltage that would normally have been applied to a tuning meter is applied to the vertical plates of the cathode-ray tube. Again, the source of this voltage may be the first or second limiter stage in the tuner i-f section. The voltage corresponding to the "S" curve of the detector—normally equal to zero when a station is correctly tuned, is applied to the horizontal-deflection circuit of the 'scope tube. Fixed voltages are

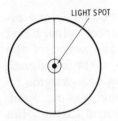

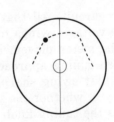

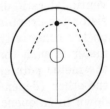

(A) *With no signal applied, spot is centered.*   (B) *As tuning is varied, spot traces i-f response of tuner.*   (C) *Station signal correctly tuned in.*

Fig. 7-12. Oscilloscope used as tuning aid.

applied to both sets of plates so that in the absence of a signal, a spot of light appears in the exact center of the viewing area. This condition is shown in Fig. 7-12A. As a station frequency is approached, the spot darts to the left (caused by, say, high negative voltage from detector output). At the same time, as the station frequency is approached, the spot moves up vertically, because of the limiter-voltage rise and continues to move back towards horizontal centering, as shown in Fig. 7-12B. As you tune further in the same direction, the light spot moves off-center to the right and, finally, dips down towards vertical center, as the station signal is lost altogether. In reality, the light spot is tracing a very good replica of the entire i-f response curve.

We mentioned that the 'scope tube indicator has uses beyond even both types of meter indicators. One of these is the ability to indicate the presence or absence of "multipath", a condition analogous to ghosts or reflections in TV reception. In the case of fm, and more particularly, stereo fm, the presence of undue amounts of multipath (usually caused by reflections from nearby structures, passing aircraft, mountains, etc.) can cause severe distortion, noise, and even cancellation of the stereo-separation effect.

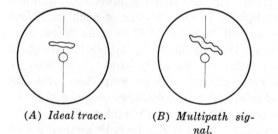

(A) Ideal trace.   (B) Multipath signal.   (C) Very severe multipath condition resulting in partial cancellation of signal.

Fig. 7-13. Oscilloscope display serves as aid in orienting antenna for best signal.

Since multipath represents a form of cancellation of signal (however momentary), and since that signal cancellation will occur at particular frequencies within the passband and not at others (because of angular phase-shift relationships), the effect of multipath may be observed on the 'scope tube. In Fig. 7-13A we see the trace caused by audio modulation. Remember that audio modulation is, effectively, a rapidly changing level of voltage, both positive and negative, about the zero center of the "S" curve of the detector. Therefore, in the presence of program material, the 'scope spot changes into a line whose length, left to right, is determined by the loudness of the program material. Fig. 7-13B shows what happens when multipath is encountered. At certain frequencies traversed during the course of audio modulation, partial cancellation takes place, reducing the amplitude of the i-f voltage, and therefore the vertical position of the trace. Fig. 7-13C illustrates a very severe case of multipath, in which almost complete cancellation takes place at certain frequencies within the desired pass-band. Such a display, incorporated in an fm tuner, serves as an aid in orienting the antenna for strongest, as well as multipath-free, signal.

MUTING AND SQUELCH CIRCUITS

Wideband fm reception which we have been investigating offers a mixed blessing when it comes to noise signals. So long as an incoming signal is of sufficient strength to cause full limiting in the limiter circuits, signal-to-noise ratios of sixty, seventy, and even eighty dB are often achieved in well-designed tuners and receivers. In the absence of such incoming signals, however, input voltage consists of random noise, usually too weak to operate the limiter at its saturation point or beyond. Under such conditions, the early i-f stages as well as the limiters act as conventional voltage amplifiers and the random, amplitude-modulated noise voltages produce the all-too-familiar hissing noise. Whether you prefer to call it background noise or interstation noise it can be both annoying and distracting when you are trying to tune to a desired station.

Many manufacturers of fm receiving equipment design and include noise-suppression systems to reduce or completely eliminate this form of disturbance. Basically, most systems involve turning off an audio stage, or the input to an audio stage in the absence of a signal of sufficient strength to effect limiting. A simple tube type circuit will illustrate one means of accomplishing interstation muting. In Fig. 7-14 the grid of an extra triode is connected to the limiter grid. The plate of this triode (V1) is connected to supply voltage, while its cath-

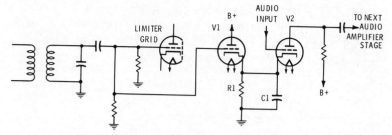

Fig. 7-14. Simple muting circuit using vacuum tubes.

ode is connected to the cathode of the first audio-amplifier tube
(V2). If the current through R1 was the cathode current of
V2 alone, the voltage across R1 would provide proper bias
voltage for linear operation of V2 as a normal audio-amplifier
stage. In the absence of any negative voltage at the grid of
V1, however, V1 conducts heavily and since its cathode is also
connected to the top of R1, the voltage developed at the cathode of V2 is sufficient to cut off V2 completely. From our earlier discussion of tube limiters you may recall that an incoming 10.7 MHz i-f signal causes an increasingly negative voltage to appear at the grid of the limiter stage. Since the grid of
V1 is connected to the grid of the limiter it, too, will become
negative, reducing total current through V1. As conduction
through V1 diminishes, voltage at the cathode of V2 returns
to a lower value and V2 conducts normally, operating as a
linear voltage amplifier and allowing the audio information to
proceed to the amplifiers that follow.

Another source of increasingly negative voltage with increased signal strength is the negative end of the storage capacitor of a ratio-detector circuit. (This circuit was analyzed
in detail in Chapter 6.) In Fig. 7-15 this negative-going point
in the circuit is shown connected to a squelch tube, V1. Again,
the cathode of V1 is tied directly to the cathode of the first
audio-amplifier tube, V2, so that the cathode bias on V2 is
caused by the sum of currents in both V1 and V2. With the
grid of V1 only slightly negative (as would be the case in the
presence of noise, but no real i-f signal), the bias voltage at
the cathode of V2 is sufficient to cut that tube off completely,
preventing the audio signal from going on to the second audio
stage. With increased signal strength, the negative end of the
ratio-detector charging capacitor becomes more negative and

the grid of V1 therefore tends to cut off the current of that tube. Once again, the bias voltage of V2 returns to normal and V2 behaves as a normal audio-amplifier stage, passing on the audio information to succeeding stages.

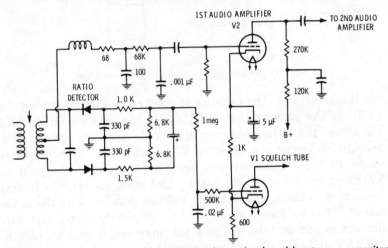

Fig. 7-15. Muting circuit utilizing negative voltage developed by storage capacitor of ratio-detector circuit.

The transition to solid-state circuitry in fm receivers required a slightly different approach to the design of muting circuits. For one thing, transistorized limiters do not develop grid-leak voltages which can be used to control other stages. Too, transistor stages are not normally cut off by applying cathode bias. Since transistors are particularly good at switching functions, however, most muting circuits use a transistor as a shunt switch, shorting out the audio recovery point when signal strength is inadequate and opening up or removing the short in the presence of sufficient signal strength.

Fig. 7-16 illustrates a simple form of muting circuit adaptable to solid-state designs. C1 couples some of the 10.7-MHz voltage from the second or third i-f stage to diode X1. In the absence of such a signal, Q1 is biased heavily into conduction because of the positive voltage applied to its base through R2. In this mode, Q1 acts like an almost complete short circuit across the ratio detector output, silencing any noise (and weak signals) that may be coming through. With a 10.7-MHz signal of sufficient amplitude applied to diode X1, however, a negative voltage is developed at the base of Q1 (filtered by means of RC network R1-C2), counteracting the fixed positive voltage at that point and cutting off Q1. Q1 then appears as an open circuit (or, more properly, a very high impedance) and no longer shunts the audio signal to ground.

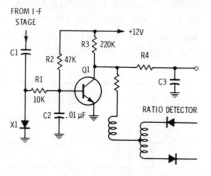

Fig. 7-16. Simple muting circuit using rectified 10.7-MHz signal to control switching transistor Q1.

There are many possible refinements of this circuit. For one thing, a potentiometer may be added at an appropriate point in the circuit to determine at what point muting shall take place. Such an addition enables the user to obtain just as much muting as he desires. If he is in an area where most of the desired signals are quite strong, he may elect to turn up the muting all the way and have absolute silence between stations. If the listener is in the unfortunate position of receiving only weak signals, he may apply only as much muting as is necessary for some reduction in noise without obliterating reception of many of his preferred stations.

A disadvantage inherent in the circuit of Fig. 7-16 is its inability to effect an instantaneous transition from "mute" to "no mute" at a given signal strength or "threshold". There is a region in which Q1 is neither a short nor an open circuit. In this region, the partial shunting effect of Q1 across the output of the ratio detector will reduce the amplitude of the recovered audio and often introduce large amounts of distortion as well. For this reason, manufacturers tend towards more sophisticated and positive-acting circuits such as that shown in Fig. 7-17.

In this partial schematic, a portion of the positive-going dc voltage developed across capacitor C212 is applied to the base of dc amplifier Q201. This npn device conducts more heavily as its base becomes more positive and the tuning meter in the collector circuit reads "up-scale" to a degree determined by the signal strength. As current increases in the collector circuit of Q201, the voltage at the junction of R218 and R220 *decreases*. As a result, the base voltage appearing at Q202 becomes less positive. When this voltage goes below 4.3 volts dc, Q202 suddenly stops conducting, because the voltage is now less positive than the zener-diode controlled 4.3 volts applied to the emitter by means of the zener-diode X202 and the dropping resistor R219.

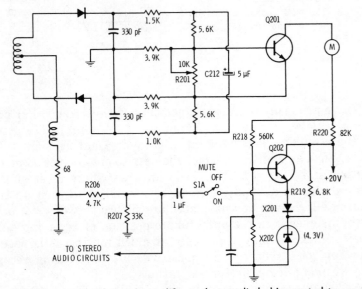

Fig. 7-17. Muting circuit using dc amplifier and zener-diode bias control to provide positive muting action.

So long as Q202 is conducting, it acts as a short circuit across the audio signal at the junction of R206 and R207, providing the desired muting effect when S1A is in the FM MUTE position. Once its base voltage becomes less positive than its emitter voltage, however, Q202, an npn device, is abruptly cut off, appearing as a high impedance or "open circuit" across the audio voltage which is passed on to the fm stereo circuits that follow. The principle, here, is similar to that discussed in connection with Fig. 7-16. The improvement lies in the fact that the mute point can now be predetermined by the setting of P201 and that the transition from total mute to no mute is abrupt—there is little or no region of signal strength at which the signal is partially muted and distorted. This circuit is actually used in a modern solid-state receiver—the Altec Lansing Model 711B.

As before, the 10.7-MHz signal itself (or its absence) can be used to develop a dc voltage which, in turn, can turn the audio signal on or off. Such a circuit is shown in Fig. 7-18, a partial schematic of the muting section of the Studio Pro 120 solid-state receiver, by University Sound. C207 couples 10.7-

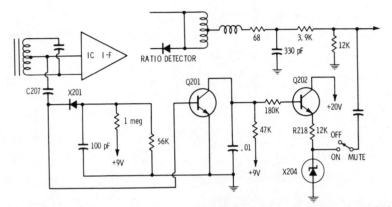

Fig. 7-18. Positive-action muting circuit using control voltage derived from rectified 10.7-MHz signal.

MHz voltage to diode X201, creating a dc voltage to add to the forward bias normally applied to the base of Q201. Collector voltage of Q201 becomes less positive than it was in the absence of signal and so does the base of Q202. As current through Q202 decreases, the voltage at the junction of R218 and X204 (a 6.8-volt zener diode) goes below the 6.8 volts required to "break down" the zener and it becomes an "open circuit", allowing the audio to go on to the multiplex decoder stages that follow.

Any number of variations for providing muting circuits are possible, depending upon the basic i-f and detection layout as well as the ingenuity of the designer. The best circuits will introduce little or no distortion or change of level in the "threshold" region. Elaborateness of design is governed by the selling price of the tuner or receiver, of course. The fact that a given tuner or receiver has *no* muting circuit is no indication of inferior quality. Some designers feel that, within a given price limitation, other features may be of greater importance to the user and so muting might be "traded off" in favor of some other feature, such as zero-center tuning meter, automatic stereo switching, etc.

Chapter 8

FM Receiver Measurements

SPECIFICATIONS

It is just about nine years since the Institute of High Fidelity (IHF) issued standards for measuring and specifying the performance of fm and fm/a-m tuners. Prior to that updating, nearly everyone involved in fm relied upon a 1947 Standard, issued by the IRE (now IEEE) entitled, *Methods of Test, Frequency Modulation Broadcast Receivers*," and its subsequent supplements. At the present time, the IHF is again actively preparing a further updating of its test specifications. These newer standards, when issued, will be very welcome, particularly in the light of newer, solid-state circuitry (which was not available in consumer products in 1958) and fm stereo (which did not become a factor in home fm receivers until late in 1961). For the present, therefore, we shall consider only those tests and specifications which appear in the 1958 IHF standard (No. IHFM-T-100) and which relate strictly to monophonic fm performance. Later, we shall suggest our own interim tests and specifications relating to fm stereo which will prove useful until such time as the new IHF standards are ready.

The specifications set forth in the 1958 Standards are divided into two categories. They include the following:

Primary Specifications

1. IHF sensitivity
2. Signal-to-noise ratio
3. Harmonic distortion
4. Drift
5. Frequency response

Secondary Specifications

6. Capture ratio
7. Selectivity
8. Spurious responses
9. IM distortion
10. Audio hum
11. A-m suppression

Manufacturers who subscribe to the IHF standards of measurement are required to list all specifications in the primary category as minimum published specifications, and all the specifications of the primary and secondary categories for "complete" specifications. If the foregoing 11 specifications fully define the performance of any fm (mono) tuner, an understanding of how these specifications are measured should be most helpful in your quest for a knowledge of what a good fm tuner is expected to do and how it is expected to do it. We shall start, therefore, with an analysis of each of the primary category specifications.

IHF Sensitivity

Prior to 1958, this specification was often called "quieting sensitivity." The set-up for making this measurement is shown in Fig. 8-1. An fm signal generator is connected to the antenna input terminals of the tuner under test. The fm generator is modulated by a 400-Hz tone to the extent of 30 percent of maximum deviation (22.5 kHz). An ac VTVM is connected at the audio output terminals of the tuner.

The number of rf microvolts applied to the tuner's antenna terminals is varied until a difference of 30 dB is noted on the meter between the modulated and unmodulated conditions. In

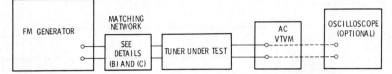

(A) *Instruments used and method of connecting them.*

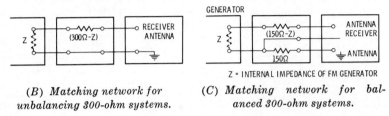

Z = INTERNAL IMPEDANCE OF FM GENERATOR

(B) *Matching network for unbalancing 300-ohm systems.*

(C) *Matching network for balanced 300-ohm systems.*

Fig. 8-1. Test setup for measuring quieting sensitivity.

the unmodulated condition, the meter is reading residual noise, of course, and the sole purpose of the old IRE specification was to denote how many microvolts it would take to produce an audio output (at 22.5-kHz modulation) which was 30 dB greater than the residual noise. Ultimately, this was modified in promotion material to "soup up" specs. It was the "22.5-kHz" deviation part of the specification that was assaulted. The reasoning was that the noise reference should be taken as "so many dB lower than the *loudest* audio possible," which would mean below a 75-kHz modulation.

Referring to Fig. 8-2 you can easily see that this added 10 dB to the signal-to-noise figure—not by any improvement in circuitry, but simply because 75 kHz of modulation results in 10 dB more audio output than does 22.5 kHz. If the noise doesn't change (and it doesn't) this means a 40 dB signal-to-noise quieting ratio. But IRE specified that a 30 dB signal-to-noise ratio was to be standard, so, with this amount of modulation during testing, it was possible to reduce the number of microvolts applied to the antenna terminals. Thus, what looked like a "6.5 microvolt" sensitivity when measured according to correct IRE practice, suddenly comes up as a 4.5 microvolt tuner under the conditions of 100 percent modulation, conceived as described.

As a further development, it was decided that a 20 dB signal-to-noise ratio was quite acceptable. If that measure of

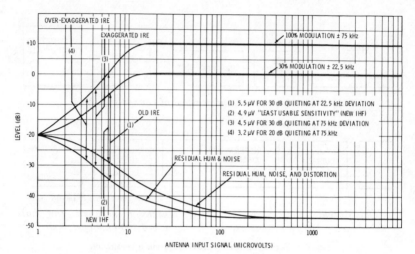

Fig. 8-2. Curves showing signal-to-noise relationships in an fm tuner.

The figure contains the following labels:

OVER-EXAGGERATED IRE
EXAGGERATED IRE
100% MODULATION ± 75 kHz
30% MODULATION ± 22.5 kHz
OLD IRE
(1) 5.5 µV FOR 30 dB QUIETING AT 22.5 kHz DEVIATION
(2) 4.9 µV "LEAST USABLE SENSITIVITY" (NEW IHF)
(3) 4.5 µV FOR 30 dB QUIETING AT 75 kHz DEVIATION
(4) 3.2 µV FOR 20 dB QUIETING AT 75 kHz
RESIDUAL HUM & NOISE
RESIDUAL HUM, NOISE, AND DISTORTION
NEW IHF
LEVEL (dB)
ANTENNA INPUT SIGNAL (MICROVOLTS)

quieting is referred to 100 percent modulation, we come up with a 3.2 microvolt tuner! Even worse, the resulting output might well be loaded with distortion and be quite unlistenable from that standpoint, but that factor did not figure in any of the earlier specification methods.

It is a general truth (though not a universal one) with most fm circuits that as the signal strength is decreased below a certain level, the bandwidth of the tuner tends to become narrower and narrower, until, finally, it is not able to linearly pass the full ±75 kHz which stations are authorized to employ for full modulation. The oscilloscope trace photo of Fig. 8-3

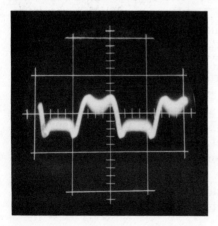

Fig. 8-3. Sine-wave response of an fm tuner having inadequate bandwidth to low-level signals.

shows what happens to a sine wave when passed through the rf, i-f, and detector circuits of an fm tuner which has an inadequate bandwidth at low signal levels. True, the signal may well be 30 or even 40 dB louder than the residual noise, in this case, but who would want to listen to such a distorted representation of a pure sine-wave tone?

Happily, the IHF Standard of 1958 did away both with the variations in the method of reporting quieting sensitivity and with the complete neglect of the distortion factor. The IHF test set-up is similar to the one shown in Fig. 8-1, except that now a distortion analyzer meter is required instead of a simple ac VTVM. The modulating tone is again 400 Hz, but this time it is set to deliberately modulate the fm generator 100 percent (75 kHz). Thus, the bandwidth capability of a tuner is tested at low signal strengths. This time, the modulation is left on all the time. But it is tuned out by null filters in the audio distortion analyzer. Consequently, any harmonics of 400 Hz *plus* noise are read. The number of microvolts applied to the antenna terminals are adjusted until the difference between full audio output and distortion-plus-noise (as read on the distortion analyzer) is 30 dB. The resulting microvolt figure necessary to accomplish this is often referred to as the "least usable sensitivity" of the tuner, a much more meaningful figure than its predecessor.

Signal-to-Noise Ratio

Since 30 dB of signal-to-noise and distortion is considered to be the "least usable" sensitivity, it is important to be able to determine what the ultimate signal-to-noise and distortion capability of a given fm tuner is. That is, under conditions of strong input signal (1000 microvolts fed to the antenna terminals), what will the residual hum and noise component be. Note, that for this measurement, distortion is deemed to be insignificant. At 1000 microvolts input, any tuner incapable of passing a fully modulated (±75 kHz) signal is hardly worth categorizing as a piece of high-fidelity equipment in the first place.

Accordingly, the method first described in the old IRE specification (See Fig. 8-1) is used, and the rating is determined by comparing the VTVM reading with no applied modulation to the reading for 100 percent modulation. The higher the signal-to-noise ratio obtained, the better the receiver or tuner. Readings of 60, 70, or even 80 dB are not uncommon among the better tuners.

You will note in Fig. 8-2, based upon our "fictitious" (and not too good, by today's standards) tuner, that the maximum signal-to-noise obtainable is only about 58 dB (read the difference between the fully modulated output, +10 dB, and the residual noise at 1000 microvolts of input, −48 dB). Then again, this imaginary tuner exhibits a "least usable" sensitivity of only 4.9 microvolts compared with actual quality tuners, both tube and solid-state, that approach an amazing 1.5 microvolts or so!

Harmonic Distortion

While the meaning of harmonic distortion remains the same whether it relates to a tuner or to an audio amplifier, the underlying cause of such distortion in a tuner output is altogether different from that associated with audio equipment. This may be appreciated by the following examples.

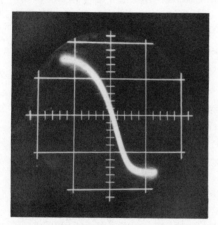

Fig. 8-4. Typical "S" curve response obtained at the output of a properly-aligned, high-quality fm tuner. Linear portion extends nearly ± 400 kHz about center frequency.

The 'scope photo of Fig. 8-4 shows the overall response of a tuner, from antenna input to demodulator output. Usually referred to as an "S" curve, this pattern is achieved by modulating an fm generator several hundreds of kHz's. The output of the tuner connects to the vertical input of an oscilloscope, while the modulating voltage used to deviate the generator is simultaneously applied to the external horizontal input of the oscilloscope. Thus, as the rf signal is made to sweep above and below the tuned frequency of the tuner under investigation, the scope traces out the instantaneous output voltage above and below the zero axis.

In the actual photo of Fig. 8-4, the modulation was nearly plus and minus 1 MHz. Therefore, the excursion from one crest of the "S" curve to the other can be estimated at about 800 kHz—a very wideband response, indeed! You can further estimate the small, but extremely linear portion of the curve that would be necessary to respond to a mere 75 kHz of deviation. This tuner, having such extremely linear response about its center frequency, will have only a minute amount of harmonic distortion in the output.

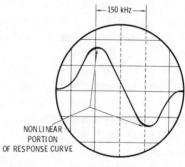

Fig. 8-5. Narrow bandpass that could cause high distortion at relatively high percentage of modulation.

If, as in the sketch of Fig. 8-5, the distance from crest to crest of the "S" curve were only about 150 kHz, then extremities of the normal ±75 kHz encountered in normal broadcasting would involve highly nonlinear portions of the response curve, resulting in a high order of harmonic-distortion percentages. The rated harmonic distortion of a tuner, according to IHF standards, is measured with a 1000-microvolt antenna-input signal under conditions of 100 percent modulation, using a 400 Hz modulating tone. It is measured with the conventional audio harmonic-distortion analyzer.

Drift

There are three causes of frequency drift in an fm tuner. What was formerly the most serious cause—the heating up of frequency-sensitive components in the local oscillator circuit—has largely been eliminated since the introduction of solid-state tuners. Another cause of drift is often due to a change in power-supply voltage.

The use of regulated power supplies in modern circuits employing zener-diode and similar regulating devices has largely reduced this form of drift as well. Finally, if the receiver is equipped with automatic gain control, the control circuit may, indirectly, cause a frequency shift with changes of signal strength. The three forms of drift must therefore be measured separately, to avoid confusion.

"Warm-up" drift, to the degree that it still exists, is measured for a two hour period, from a "cold" start. The first reading is taken after one minute of operation. The variation in frequency for this test is seen with a beat signal obtained between the fm signal generator and another oscillator of constant frequency. The frequency of the primary signal generator is first adjusted so that the tuner or receiver is correctly tuned. The beat frequency is measured and recorded, as is the subsequent change in generator frequency with time to achieve the same beat frequency.

For the effect of voltage variation on drift, the supply voltage is varied from 105 volts to 125 volts and the amount of frequency shift which occurs for this change of line voltage is stated.

For frequency shift relating to agc control circuits, the signal input is varied from the "least usable sensitivity" all the way up to 100,000 microvolts. Any attendant frequency shift is recorded. The rated frequency drift of the tuner or receiver is the largest of the three drifts measured.

Frequency Response

This test has the same meaning as it does with any piece of audio equipment. It is performed by applying a series of modulating frequencies from 50 Hz to 15 kHz (the limits for fm broadcasting). Unless you understand pre-emphasis and de-emphasis in fm broadcasting and reception, you will be astounded to find that the response of a perfectly-adjusted tuner will look exactly like the curve shown in Fig. 8-6.

The need for pre-emphasis and de-emphasis was discussed in Chapter 2. You will recall that during the transmission process, all frequencies above approximately 1000 Hz were boosted in accordance with the curve of Fig. 2-12 in order to improve the signal-to-noise ratio at the receiving end. By attenuating the higher frequencies in receiver circuits as shown in Fig. 8-6, flat or uniform response (considered from microphone to speaker) is restored. Most fm signal generators do not have built-in pre-emphasis circuits, and therefore they differ in this respect from actual transmitter set-ups. It is for this reason that frequency-response curves taken by using an fm generator connected to the antenna terminals will yield results as shown in Fig. 8-6.

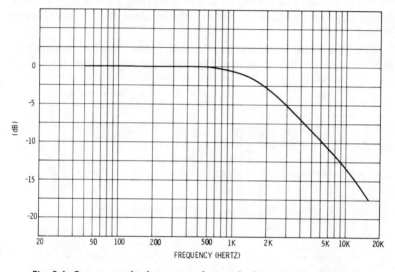

Fig. 8-6. Correct standard response of properly de-emphasized fm tuner.

Thus far we have examined the so-called "Primary" fm specifications which, according to the Standard of the Institute of High Fidelity (IHFM-T-100), are the least number of specifications needed to describe the performance of an fm tuner. The serious-minded fm devotee will, of course, want to know much more about the performance of his fm tuner or receiver. The so-called "Secondary" specifications, listed earlier in this chapter, should therefore be of equal interest.

Capture Ratio

The capture-ratio test is designed to show the effect of an interfering signal that has the same frequency as the desired signal. You may recall that the least usable sensitivity was defined as the number of microvolts input to a receiver or tuner required to produce an output (under conditions of 100 percent modulation) 30 dB greater than any residual noise or distortion. This figure of 30 dB is a significant one. It will be used again in the capture-ratio test, for it is considered to be the least difference between "wanted" and "unwanted" components of a signal which make that signal minimally acceptable. In the case of the "capture-ratio" test, however, we are interested in knowing how much more powerful our *desired* signal must be, compared to the interfering signal at the same frequency, to produce 30 dB of attenuation of the interfering signal.

The test setup is shown in Fig. 8-7. Note that *two* accurately calibrated fm signal generators are required, but that only

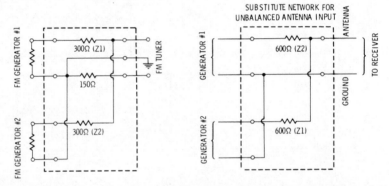

Fig. 8-7. Test setup for performing capture-ratio and selectivity tests. Z_1 and Z_2 match the internal impedances of the generators.

one need be capable of being modulated in an fm manner. Thus, a laboratory having an fm generator and an accurate a-m generator (whose frequencies extend to 100 MHz and above) calibrated in microvolts output could perform the test as well.

To maintain a proper 300-ohm matching impedance between the two generators and a balanced 300-ohm input of a typical receiver, the resistive network shown in the diagram is required. Due to the attenuation introduced by this network, however, all microvolt readings as shown on the generators should be divided by two, since only one-half the number of microvolts is actually reaching the receiver under test.

To obtain rated capture ratio, a 1000-microvolt, 100 per-cent-modulated (400 Hz) signal is applied to the receiver from the generator capable of being frequency modulated. The audio output voltage from the detector is noted. Next, the second generator is brought into play, and its signal is increased until the audio output voltage from the receiver is reduced by just 1 dB.

As an example, suppose it takes 1200 microvolts to accomplish this. Record this number. Then increase the microvolt output from the second, unmodulated generator until the audio output falls another 29 dB, or a total of 30 dB. Record this number of microvolts, which we'll assume is 2400 microvolts. The capture ratio is the ratio of these two readings, in deci-bels, divided by two. Thus, in our illustration, 2400/1200 = 2/1 = 6 dB; 6 dB/2 = 3 dB. The rated capture ratio would be stated as 3 dB and gives the ratio of desired to undesired sig-nal necessary to suppress the undesired signal by 30 dB.

The test is usually repeated at test frequencies of 90, 98 and 106 MHz, and the worst figure (highest number of decibels) is the published rated capture ratio.

In the event that the receiver under test has a 300-ohm un-balanced (or grounded) input, the resistive network required between the two generators and the receiver under test is also shown in Fig. 8-7. Generator readings are still divided by two in this case.

Selectivity

The tests categorized under this heading concern determin-ing the ability of a receiver to reject an unwanted signal from an adjacent station while accepting the desired station.

While the tests may be conducted using frequencies 200 kHz apart (one channel), a more realistic approach is to separate the desired and undesired frequencies by 400 kHz (two chan-nels). This is so because the FCC does not assign station fre-quencies 200 kHz apart to any two stations in a given geo-graphical location.

The test set-up for determining rated selectivity is exactly the same as that used for capture ratio tests, but the procedure is different. First, the "interfering" fm generator is now the one which can be frequency modulated, and it is tuned away from the "desired" signal generator setting and the receiver setting by 400 kHz. The unmodulated generator output is increased to a value of 100 microvolts. The "detuned" (by 400 kHz) generator is modulated 100 percent, and its output is increased until an output from the receiver is obtained which is 30 dB below the output that would be obtained were it tuned to the frequency of the receiver.

As an example, suppose "normal" full audio output from the detector is 1 volt, under conditions of 100 percent modulation. The detuned generator's output would be increased until an output of .03 volt (30 dB below 1 volt) is noted at the detector output of the receiver under test. Suppose, further, that the output of the detuned generator had to be advanced to 10,000 microvolts before this minute interfering signal was noted. The ratio of the two generator outputs, expressed in decibels, would be: 10,000/100 = 40 dB. The "rated" selectivity would therefore be published by the manufacturer of the receiver as "40 dB."

To translate this back to more meaningful terms, this means that a station 400 kHz removed from our desired station, would have to be received by our antenna with a signal strength 100 times more powerful than the desired station to cause an interference signal 30 dB lower than the desired signal. Such situations arise frequently, of course, as there are very distant and local stations in any given area. The higher the selectivity (in decibels) the greater the difference in signal strength required before a strong station will interfere with our sometimes-desired weaker station.

Since decibel notations are logarithmic, an increase in selectivity of just another 10 dB (in the example cited) to, say, 50 dB selectivity, would mean that the interfering station would have to be received at a signal strength of 100,000 microvolts (much less likely) to cause perceptible interference with our puny 100 microvolt "desired" signal!

Spurious Responses

Virtually all fm tuners or receivers are of the superheterodyne type. That is, they involve the use of a local oscillator which beats with the incoming signal to produce a lower, intermediate frequency, generally 10.7 MHz. While many spurious responses (output from the receiver even though it is tuned to some frequency other than the generator frequency) are possible, two particularly significant spurious responses are usually measured first. These are "image response" and "i-f response."

Image response may best be understood by examining Fig. 8-8. In this illustration, the desired station, located at 103.1 MHz, is selected by means of the tuning knob on the receiver. Assume, for the moment, that the local oscillator of this receiver is set 10.7 MHz below the tuned frequency, at 92.4 MHz. Incoming frequencies will, of course, beat with the local oscillator whether they are above it in frequency (like the desired station at 103.1) or below it! Now, it so happens that exactly 10.7 MHz *below* our local oscillator is 81.7 MHz. This is outside the fm band, but right in the middle of the sound channel of TV Channel 5.

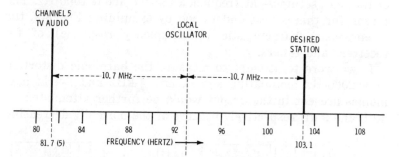

Fig. 8-8. Image frequency and desired station are separated by two times the intermediate frequency. Local oscillator lies halfway between the two.

All right, you say, design the local oscillator so that it is 10.7 MHz *above* the desired frequency. Most receivers do just that, but that throws the image frequency at a point anywhere from 109.4 MHz to 129.4 MHz, right in the range of aircraft navigation frequencies.

The other predominant spurious response is at the intermediate frequency itself (usually 10.7 MHz). There is much broadcasting taking place at a primary frequency of around 10 MHz. As a result, these direct signals may well by-pass the rf and converter sections of a receiver and be amplified directly by the 10.7-MHz stages. Finally, a given receiver may be responsive to all sorts of harmonics, sub-harmonics, and other frequencies mathematically related to the one being tuned in.

In evaluating a receiver in terms of spurious responses, each of the possible interfering frequencies is selected on a signal generator and the sensitivity is measured as in the "least usable sensitivity" test described previously, with one exception: with no modulation applied, the tuner output is adjusted to the same output obtained in the usable sensitivity test with modulation removed. The ratio of generator output for the spurious response and the generator output required for the usual 30-dB usable sensitivity is calculated and expressed in decibels.

Distortion

Harmonic-distortion measurements taken with a single modulating frequency (just as in audio circuit evaluation) are of limited usefulness at frequencies above about 1000 Hz. The reason for this is best understood by examining Fig. 8-9, the de-emphasis characteristic (or frequency response) of fm receivers and tuners.

If we were to attempt to measure the harmonic distortion of a 2000-Hz modulating signal, any 4-kHz and 8-kHz harmonics present in the output would be further attenuated by 4 dB and 9 dB respectively because of the normally decreasing

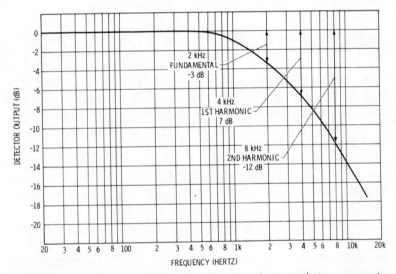

Fig. 8-9. De-emphasis characteristic of an fm tuner, showing relative attentuation of a fundamental and its first and second harmonics.

response of the tuner, giving rise to totally erroneous readings. Of course, under broadcast conditions, these higher frequencies are pre-emphasized, so that the overall response of the system (from transmitter to loudspeaker) is flat.

Accordingly, the rated harmonic distortion of an fm tuner or receiver is determined by modulating the signal generator at 400 Hz only, at 75-kHz deviation (100 percent). The generator is adjusted to provide a 1000-microvolt rf input signal to the set under test, so that noise is no longer a significant factor in the measurement.

Intermodulation distortion testing is best for describing deficiencies of the set at higher modulating frequencies. Unlike the equivalent test applied to audio equipment, the two input modulating frequencies required are only 400 Hz apart —15,000 Hz and 14,600 Hz. Furthermore, both modulating signals are equal in amplitude, and together modulate the signal generator to 100 percent deviation. The generator output is set to 1000 microvolts once more and the resultant 400 Hz produced by the non-linearity of the circuits is measured at the output of the receiver's detector. This measurement is expressed as a percentage of the 400-Hz output that would be obtained if the generator were modulated with 400 Hz at full deviation.

Audio Hum

As would be expected, this measurement is similar to its counterpart in audio work. The total output of the tuner is measured with the tuner tuned to a 1000-microvolt signal at 98 MHz (the generator is not modulated). The results are expressed as the number of decibels below 100 percent modulation, at the same signal strength. Needless to say, the rf generator should itself be free of any hum modulation of its rf oscillator, or this will show up as hum in the output of the receiver.

A-M Suppression

Obviously, the better an fm system is able to reject a-m, the more noise-free it will be, insofar as man-made and natural static are concerned. To measure rated amplitude suppression, an a-m generator capable of producing frequencies at 98 MHz is required. A signal 10 dB higher than the "least usable sensitivity" signal is applied to the set under test, with 100 percent frequency modulation at 400 Hz. The output voltage is recorded. Next, a 400-Hz null filter is inserted between the output of the tuner and the meter, and the generator is amplitude modulated to 30 percent (amplitude modulation) at 1000 Hz. The undesired output obtained is expressed in decibels below the fm output obtained in the first reading.

Future Standards

As you can see, tests of monophonic fm tuners and receivers have been well defined and, in general, carefully observed and standardized by the reputable manufacturers of fm tuners and receivers. Naturally, in the course of an actual primary design, there are many more tests and evaluations that are made at an engineering level. Still, the specifications described thus far are nearly ten years old, and were promulgated long before stereo fm came upon the scene.

FM STEREO MEASUREMENTS

Universally-accepted standards of measurement and rating for fm stereo have not yet been adopted by the IHF or any other recognized group within the audio industry. Nevertheless, with fm stereo tuners and receivers well entrenched as part of the high fidelity scene (not to mention the "package" or console equipment which also boasts fm stereo) most manufacturers have individually selected what they consider to be the defining specifications relating to fm stereo reception, having listed such "specs" along with the more standard tuner and amplifier criteria.

It is from these voluntary listings, as well as from our own experience with the new medium, that we shall list what might be considered the minimum specifications (until a standard comes along) in defining fm stereo performance. Then we shall examine methods of measurements which are proposed as standard procedure, so that everyone's results will be consistent with everyone else's.

Primary FM Stereo Specifications

1. Rated separation, left and right channels.
   A. Midband

B. High frequency

C. Low frequency

2. Least usable stereo sensitivity
3. Separation stability
4. Fm stereo harmonic distortion
5. Subcarrier, subharmonic, and harmonic rejection
6. SCA rejection
7. Stereo indicator sensitivity

Rated Separation

The FCC requires that a station broadcasting fm stereo transmit left and right channels with separation in excess of 30 dB. This corresponds to about 3 percent of left channel information getting into the right channel and vice versa. What is more, this capability must extend over the entire audio spectrum, from 50 Hz to 15,000 kHz.

While few receivers on the market can duplicate such separation, it must be said that separation figures of lesser magnitude still yield a highly satisfactory stereo illusion. However, continued degrading of separation ultimately destroys the stereo effect for many people. Just how much separation and over what band of frequencies is necessary is still a subject of debate. To measure separation, however requires a quality fm stereo signal simulator as well as the usual fm rf signal generator used with mono fm measurements.

Though many inexpensive "combination" pieces of equipment are available (combining a rudimentary rf signal, modulated by a properly-constituted fm stereo composite signal), the rf portion is usually devoid of any means of accurately calibrating microvolt input to the antenna of the equipment under test. Since fm stereo usable sensitivity is our second most important specification, this type of all-in-one equipment would not be usable for this purpose.

The test setup is illustrated in Fig. 8-10. Often, the composite fm stereo signal simulator will also contain several audio modulating frequencies for application to either left or right channel. In such cases, the separate audio oscillator can be eliminated.

Normally, a correctly constituted "left-only" signal is applied to the external modulation terminals of the fm generator. Readings are taken from both the left and right outputs of the fm stereo decoder circuitry, at a deviation or modulation of approximately 45 kHz. The frequency of the modulating left-only signal is varied over the usual range (50 Hz to

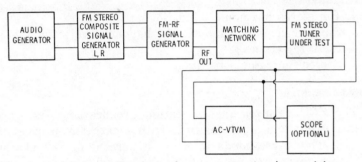

Fig. 8-10. Test setup for plotting fm stereo separation characteristics.

15,000 Hz) and a double plot such as that shown by the solid lines in Fig. 8-11 is made of the results. The procedure is repeated, applying a "right-only" signal, and the results are

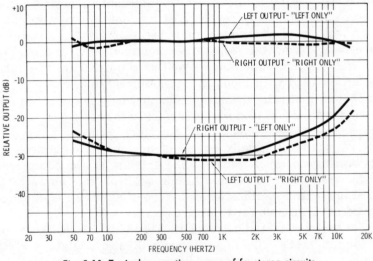

Fig. 8-11. Typical separation curves of fm stereo circuits.

plotted on the same graph (as shown by the dashed lines). The reader can, at a glance, determine separation capability from left to right, or right to left, at any frequency. Three frequencies are of interest: 1000 Hz (midband), 10 kHz (high frequency) and 100 Hz (low frequency). It would be well to use a standard input signal (rf) of 1000 microvolts, since separation may often vary with input signal strength. Further, the worst of the two curves, or that exhibiting the least separation (be it left into right or right into left), could be used in formulating a written specification. Thus, the "rated" separation might be stated as: 30 dB midband, 26 dB high-frequency, 24 dB low-frequency.

Stereo Sensitivity

As with mono fm, a program whose highest level is 30 dB above any audible noise and distortion is considered marginally satisfactory. Unfortunately, in the case of stereo, it takes more microvolts of rf input signal to produce such a noise free, distortion-free signal than would be the case in mono reception. It is for this reason that many converts to fm stereo are surprised to find that a signal strength long deemed adequate in a given location to produce noise-free reception is altogether unsatisfactory for fm stereo. The usual remedy is the installation of an outdoor antenna, if none has been used; or, in extreme cases, a more sensitive receiver turns out to be the only solution.

Least usable fm stereo sensitivity should, essentially, be measured in the same manner as the equivalent mono fm specification, with one significant exception. The normal "left" or "right" outputs of a decoded stereo signal will contain varying amounts of signal frequencies at 19 kHz, 38 kHz, and harmonics of these frequencies. In the normal fm sensitivity measurement procedure, these might show up as residual distortion if only a distortion analyzer is used. A sharp cutoff filter is therefore recommended (featuring a cutoff frequency at 15 kHz). The filter would be interposed between the output of the set under test and the distortion analyzer.

Since we wish to employ full 75-kHz deviation of the main carrier to correspond to the monophonic test procedure, a "left-right" signal (plus the required 19-kHz pilot signal) should be used to modulate the fm generator, rather than a "left only" "right only" signal, as in previous separation tests. Readings may therefore be taken at either the left- or right-channel outputs of the decoder section. A block diagram of the proposed test setup is shown in Fig. 8-12.

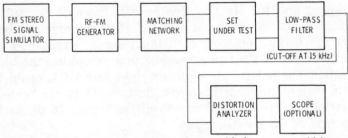

Fig. 8-12. Test setup to determine least usable fm stereo sensitivity.

Separation Stability

Optimum rated separation is dependent upon many factors, not the least of which is a requirement that the input signal be sufficient to cause full limiting of the receiver. At signal inputs of lesser strength, the amplitude of the incoming 19-kHz pilot signal may be insufficient to cause either proper locking of the local 38-kHz oscillator (restored carrier) or, in the absence of such an oscillator (as in the directly-amplified and doubled 19-kHz circuits), improper phase relationships between the stereo audio information and the reconstituted 38-kHz subcarrier. In such cases, ultimate separation will suffer. The purpose of this test, therefore, is to determine at what signal strength the separation is degraded by 3 dB.

The procedure involves a repetition of the test setup shown in Fig. 8-10. This time, signal strength is gradually reduced until separation decreases (in either channel) by 3 dB. Thus, if original rated separation was 30 dB at midband, signal strength is reduced until separation at midband is only 27 dB. If the number of microvolts being applied exceeds "least usable fm stereo sensitivity," then this number of microvolts determines the separation stability. The rating may be written thus: "separation stability: 10 microvolts or more."

If, on the other hand, the decrease in separation does not occur all the way down to "least usable fm stereo sensitivity" microvolts, then this specification becomes academic, and the rating would read: "Separation stability: Totally stable at all signal strengths."

Harmonic Distortion

Since additional circuitry is involved in the re-creation of an identifiable "left" and "right" signal at the output of an

134

fm stereo tuner, there are additional sources of harmonic distortion. Certain characteristics of the composite stereo signal itself also render it more susceptible to distortion products. Thus, a new distortion rating is needed for this type of equipment.

To impose really tight demands upon the circuitry, we suggest that the signal applied during the distortion measurement be an "L = − R" signal which shall modulate the fm generator to 90 percent of full deviation. The remaining 10 percent modulation shall, of course, be produced by the ever-present 19-kHz signal. Readers may argue that such a signal hardly ever occurs under broadcast conditions, but our counterargument is that it may *possibly* occur, and since it constitutes the most difficult signal to handle (from the point of view of distortion), why not use it—so long as all manufacturers use the very same signal. In any event, the rated distortion shall be the distortion read at either the left or right outputs, with a sharp cutoff filter (above 15 kHz) interposed between the output and the distortion analyzer. Signal strength, for the test, shall be a full 1000 microvolts, so that noise is not a contributing factor to the reading.

Subcarrier and Harmonic Rejection

Left- and right-channel information recovery is not unlike simple a-m detection. Much has been written about fm stereo demodulation, interpreting it as matrix circuitry, switching circuitry, envelope detection, and so on.

The photo of Fig. 8-13 shows a composite signal just before demodulation. If you are at all familiar with amplitude-modulation waveforms, it will seem odd to you that an envelope is traced out on one edge of the total waveform. The fact is, that this photo represents a "left only" signal about to be demodulated. Fig. 8-14, its counterpart, represents—you guessed it—a right-only signal about to undergo demodulation. Just as it is necessary to filter out any 455-kHz i-f signal after the a-m information has been detected in an a-m radio, so is it necessary to attenuate the subcarrier frequency involved in the fm stereo composite signal—38 kHz. Not that this frequency could be heard by the listener if it were allowed to go on to the audio amplifier and loudspeakers! It is too high in frequency for that. If present in sufficient amplitude, however, it

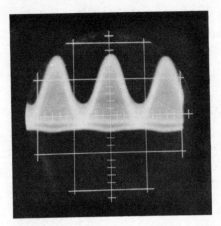

Fig. 8-13. Composite "left-only" signal prior to demodulation. Audio information consists of upper envelope on 38 kHz restored subcarrier.

could conceivably damage tweeters. Too, since it usually contains an abundance of harmonics (76 kHz, and so on), one or more of these frequencies might be close in frequency to that of the bias oscillator of your favorite tape recorder (on which you plan to record that "perfect" library from your favorite fm stereo station). Resultant recordings might contain an audible beat tone, arising from the heterodyning effect of the two ultrasonic frequencies.

For these reasons, it is desirable that all ultrasonic frequencies associated with the recovery of stereo-channels information be attenuated in the output as far as possible. We suggest that the rated attenuation be the number of decibels below 100 percent modulation that are measured in the absence of stereo modulating tones other than the usual 19-kHz pilot

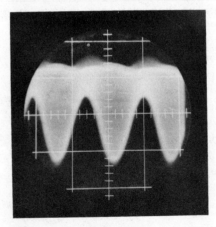

Fig. 8-14. Composite "right-only" signal prior to demodulation.

signal. In this case, the low-pass filter is removed and the meter is connected directly to the output of the receiver under test. 100 percent modulation is first applied (in the form of a full-modulation mono signal, plus 19 kHz) and the output noted. With the mono signal turned off, the output is again noted (19 kHz still being present, of course, to actuate the stereo circuitry).

The rated rejection of subcarrier and subharmonic and harmonic signals is then expressed in decibels representing the ratio of the unwanted signals to the 100 percent modulation reading at the output.

SCA Rejection

Long before stereo fm was authorized by the FCC, there was a form of "multiplex" transmission approved for use on existing fm stations which enabled the simultaneous transmission of regular public programming along with "private" subscriber programs, such as background music (to restaurants and other public places). This latter form of transmission cannot be received on conventional fm receivers, but goes out over the air as a sort of "piggy-back" arrangement. A carrier having a frequency of 67 kHz is involved, and authority to continue this private service was granted by the FCC even in the case of a station also broadcasting stereo.

As you can appreciate, a receiver equipped for fm stereo reception must have pretty flat response throughout its decoder circuitry all the way to 53 kHz, which is perilously close to the "private" service at 67 kHz. Filters must therefore be incorporated in the receiver circuitry which will eliminate any cross-talk effects from the SCA (Subsidiary Communications Authorization) programming. Such cross-talk, by the way, does not come through as recognizable audio intelligence, but as a series of whistles or "whooshing" sounds which can be annoying to a stereo listener (even at 30 dB below program content). A standard rating of SCA rejection could be obtained by modulating an fm generator with all frequencies from 60 kHz to 75 kHz, with 10 percent (7.5 kHz) deviation of the main carrier. The highest reading resulting at the output of the stereo decoder circuitry (either left or right channel) may be taken relative to 100 percent modulation output. In making these measurements, the 19-kHz pilot signal associated with the stereo composite signal must remain "on" to actuate the stereo decoding circuits in the receiver under test.

Stereo Indicator Sensitivity

Most modern stereo fm tuners and receivers include some form of visual indicator (such as a lamp) to denote the presence of a stereo signal. These should be rated in terms of the minimum number of microvolts required to actuate these devices, if that number exceeds the "least usable fm stereo sensitivity" figure described earlier. The same type of rating could be applied to the so-called "automatic switching" circuits which actuate the stereo decoding circuits in the presence of an *adequate* stereo signal.

Since stereo requires more signal input strength than mono, these circuits usually do not work in the presence of a weak, noisy signal. Accordingly, the consumer should know how many microvolts of signal strength are required to actuate the stereo circuitry, for if this number is greater than the "least usable fm stereo sensitivity" rating, it will govern the actual *stereo* performance of the receiver. If, however, the automatic circuits are capable of being defeated by a front panel switch, then this last specification need not be stated.

Chapter 9

FM Receiver Alignment

There are three general methods currently used to align the fm circuitry of either an fm tuner or the fm portion of a complete receiver. The first involves the use of relatively inexpensive test equipment, such as an amplitude-modulated rf generator and a vacuum-tube voltmeter. The second involves the use of more sophisticated equipment such as a frequency-modulated rf generator and an oscilloscope. The final method will be mentioned once, and then quickly forgotten, we trust. This method involves the "ear-to-the-loudspeaker/screw-driver-to-the-alignment-points" approach which we have, regrettably, observed from time to time. A really experienced service technician can sometimes get away with this approach in aligning a simple a-m transistor radio—using known stations as a signal source. Even then, the final alignment job will not equal that attainable with the use of proper instruments. In the case of fm receiving equipment, this hit-or-miss approach will lead to a "miss" 99 times out of 100—so don't even try it!

Before proceeding to the actual job of alignment, some generalizations can be made as to the order of the various alignment steps. Most manufacturers will advise that the detector (whether it is a discriminator or a ratio-detector) be aligned first. This is usually followed by a complete i-f alignment.

Finally, the rf or "front end" section is aligned. Often, the i-f section and detector are aligned in a single procedure, depending upon circuitry, available test points, and the individual preferences of the manufacturer. The owner of a fine tuner or receiver would do well to equip himself with the service manual supplied by the manufacturer. If this valuable booklet is not included with the manual of operating instructions, it is usually available at a slight cost directly from the manufacturer. Having this manual available when it is needed is well worth the slight expense. A good many manufacturers include the necessary alignment information at no charge along with the operating instruction booklet. We shall examine a typical example of "manufacturer's alignment instructions" after we have generalized the procedure.

I-F AND DETECTOR ALIGNMENT

Fig. 9-1 is a very generalized block diagram of an fm tuner. The receiver in question may be either of solid-state or tube construction. The detector in this diagram takes the form of a ratio detector, though later we shall repeat that part of the alignment which involves the detector stage, using a discriminator and detailing the differences in procedure required.

To align the i-f-detector portion of the receiver using just an a-m rf generator and a VTVM, the generator is set to a frequency of 10.7 MHz. The output of the generator is coupled to point A of Fig. 9-1 through an isolating capacitor (generally 0.01 μF or even smaller), so that the dc voltages at the input to the first i-f stage will not be upset or altered. The VTVM is set to a low-voltage dc scale (5 volts, or even 1.5

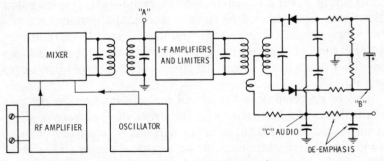

Fig. 9-1. Test points for i-f and detector alignment.

volts full-scale) and connected to point B (one side of the charging or storage capacitor of the ratio-detector circuit).

It is assumed that this tuner has conventional i-f transformers (as opposed to the newer crystal or ceramic filters), each of which has a tuning adjustment in the primary and secondary circuits. The signal generator should be adjusted to provide just enough rf output at 10.7 MHz to cause the VTVM to read part-way up the scale. As adjustments are made in each i-f interstage transformer, the output of the generator should be backed off whenever a higher reading is obtained on the meter. Each transformer is adjusted until a maximum reading is obtained on the meter. Normally, it is usual to adjust the earlier i-f transformers first, going right down the line towards the detector in the same way that the signal itself proceeds through successive i-f stages. It is extremely important to keep "backing off" the output of the signal generator as each stage is adjusted for maximum gain at 10.7 MHz. If this is not done, the i-f system will soon be well into full limiting and it becomes difficult to discern well-defined maxima as the adjustments proceed.

It is good practice after all the i-f transformers have been peaked, to repeat the process, trimming up each transformer primary and secondary to achieve absolute maximum reading on the VTVM. Only the *primary* of the ratio-detector transformer is adjusted at this time. The a-m generator used in this procedure should be capable of being attenuated to only a few microvolts output and this part of the alignment is done with no modulation applied.

Once you are certain that the i-f transformers have been optimally peaked, move the VTVM probe to point C or to the point marked "Audio" in Fig. 9-1. If your VTVM has facilities for moving the pointer to center scale electronically, do so, still keeping the range setting on the lowest, most sensitive scale. Adjust the *secondary* of the ratio-detector transformer until precisely zero volts is read on the meter. Do not make the mistake of de-tuning the secondary so far as to be completely outside the frequency range, as such a setting will also result in a zero or near zero reading. The desired zero reading is one which occurs between a positive and a negative swing of the meter. That is why it is easiest to perform this adjustment with a zero-center meter. Even a slight movement of the tuning-adjustment slug in either direction will cause a rapid movement of the meter pointer to one side or the other, about zero center.

ALIGNMENT OF DISCRIMINATORS

One form of discriminator detector is shown in Fig. 9-2. Points B and C are designated to correspond to the equivalent points used in the ratio detector of Fig. 9-1. Procedure is pretty much the same. Point B is used for peak alignment of the i-f transformer primaries and secondaries and the discriminator primary, while point C is used for zero-centering the voltage by adjustment of the secondary of the discriminator transformer.

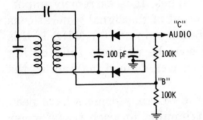

Fig. 9-2. Typical discriminator circuit with B and C test points corresponding to B and C points in Fig. 9-1.

Table 9-1 shows how a manufacturer might designate the above procedure in tabular form. Designations A11 through A18 refer to schematic designation points that correspond to the various primaries and secondaries of the i-f transformers and the ratio-detector transformer.

ALIGNMENT USING AN OSCILLOSCOPE

The well equipped service shop generally will not align fm sets (particularly high-fidelity units) using the generator-meter method outlined above. For one thing, the simpler method presumes that each i-f transformer is to be tuned to exactly 10.7 MHz when, in fact, some manufacturers require that specific stages be stagger tuned to specific frequencies other than 10.7 MHz. In this way they are able to achieve the wideband response so necessary for distortion-free audio recovery and good stereo-multiplex decoding. Even if the manufacturer were to list specific frequencies for each i-f transformer (e.g. T1—10.75 MHz; T2—10.67 MHz; T3—

Table 9-1. VTVM Alignment

FM IF ALIGNMENT USING AM SIGNAL GENERATOR – SELECTOR IN FM POSITION

High side of generator thru .01mfd to pin 2 (grid) of FM Mixer, low side to chassis.

	GENERATOR FREQUENCY	DIAL SETTING	INDICATOR	ADJUST	REMARKS
4.	10.7MC (Unmod.)	Point of non-interference.	DC probe of VTVM to point Ⓑ, common to chassis.	A11, A12 A13, A14 A15, A16 A17	Adjust for maximum.
5.	"	"	DC probe to point Ⓒ, common to chassis.	A18	Adjust for zero reading. A positive or negative reading will be obtained on either side of the correct setting.

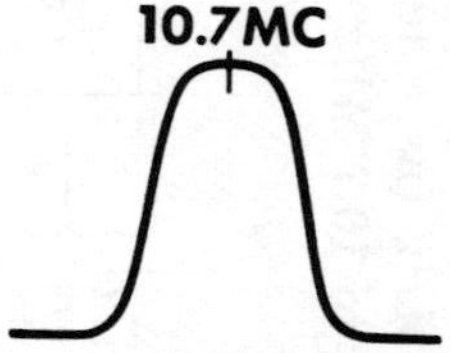

10.7MC

FIG. 1

10.7 MHz), the usual inexpensive a-m rf generator normally found in service shops is incapable of such accuracy. Normally, you're lucky if 10.7 MHz (as read on an inexpensive rf generator) is even close to 10.7 MHz in fact.

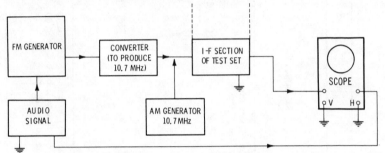

Fig. 9-3. Test setup for visual i-f alignment.

A much better method of alignment involves a visual display of the entire i-f response, made possible by the use of an oscilloscope and an fm rf sweep generator. Fig. 9-3 is a block diagram of the test setup required. The generator must be capable of producing fm output, variable in amplitude from perhaps just a few microvolts to several tenths of a volt. The modulating frequency, whether applied externally or provided by a built-in audio oscillator, must be able to shift the carrier frequency at least ± 200 kHz. Notice that the audio modulating frequency is applied to the horizontal input of the oscilloscope. The vertical input to the scope is actually taking the place of the VTVM used in the previous discussion. The unmodulated a-m rf generator used previously can now prove useful in providing a reference or marker frequency at 10.7 MHz, as will be shown shortly.

To view the overall i-f response of the tuner in question, the vertical input to the scope may be connected to the final limiter grid (in the case of tube sets), to point B of Fig. 9-1 (provided the storage or charging capacitor of the ratio detector is temporarily disconnected), or to an agc (automatic gain control) voltage point, provided agc voltage is developed from the last i-f stage or limiter.

The oscilloscope sweep selector is set to "external", thereby defeating all internal horizontal-sweep circuits. Horizontal movement of the scope trace will be governed strictly by the positive- and negative-swinging audio sinewave used to modulate the rf carrier. To clarify, let us suppose that positive-going voltage causes the trace to move to the right while negative-going voltage causes it to move to the left. Let us also suppose that positive-going audio voltage causes the rf signal in the generator to move *up* in frequency while negative-going audio causes a downward shift in carrier frequency. Fig. 9-4 relates all these movements of scope trace and frequency in a graphic manner, showing where the trace will be for a given frequency (rf) and where the frequency will be at every point in the audio-modulating cycle.

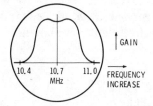

Fig. 9-4. Alignment response curve showing change in amplification (vertical) with change in frequency (horizontal).

We have noted, previously, that most i-f systems have a bandpass characteristic that is about 200 to 300 kHz wide. That is, maximum gain occurs at exactly 10.7 MHz (when everything is properly tuned up) and remains fairly constant (though not perfectly so) for about 100 kHz on either side of 10.7 MHz, falling off rapidly beyond these points.

By having the trace of the scope move along with the changing rf signal, and with the vertical input responding to amplification of the i-f system, the scope trace is made to display, repetitively, the typical i-f response curve that we have shown so many times (shown again in Fig. 9-5). By coupling the rf generator loosely to the system, a marker "pip" is introduced on the curve as shown in Fig. 9-5 and can be used as an aid in determining that the system is, in fact, centered about 10.7 MHz. By altering the frequency setting

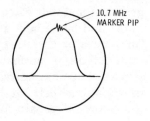

Fig. 9-5. I-f response curve with 10.7-MHz marker.

of the unmodulated auxiliary generator, it is possible to move this "pip" along the response curve to determine just how wide the bandwidth is, etc. Energy from the marker generator should be just sufficient to create a small marker in the display. If the marker signal is too strong, it will fairly well obliterate the response curve trace by taking over completely. Usually, just holding the rf output cable near the system will provide sufficient marker indication. It should be noted that some fm generators have markers of fixed frequency built right in, as an added feature.

Now, it is easy to see that correct alignment can be discerned at a glance and, what is more important, incorrect alignment, as shown in various forms in Fig. 9-6, is equally

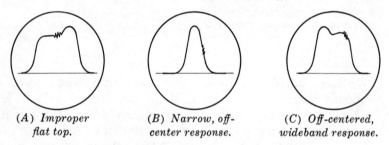

| (A) Improper flat top. | (B) Narrow, off-center response. | (C) Off-centered, wideband response. |

Fig. 9-6. Displays of misaligned i-f sections.

easy to spot. Such might not be the case in the generator-meter alignment method discussed earlier. Using this visual method, it is also possible to observe such other pertinent phenomena as the effect of varying signal strength on bandwidth, the shifting of center frequency of alignment with increased signal strength, overload characteristics of a given i-f system (how does the response curve hold up when really huge rf signals are applied) and many, many more. In short, the fm-generator-oscilloscope method of i-f and detector alignment is by far the more sophisticated and effective of the two practical methods discussed here. Why, then, do so few service shops and home labs use this method? Simply because a good fm generator costs a great deal of money—well over a thousand dollars, if purchased new. Considering the fact that most service shops have already had to spend a great deal of money in equipping their establishment, first for TV repair and then for color TV repair, it is not surprising that they don't all rush right out to purchase a $1500.00 generator. Too bad, too, since most shops have oscilloscopes equal to this particular task. The test equipment manufacturer who develops a good fm generator for under $200.00 will do the high fidelity industry a great service. While a great many fm generators do appear in the trade catalogs for even less than this figure, do not be misled. All they are good for is a spot-check of frequency calibration and a very rudimentary kind of alignment usage. Their problem lies in their inability to provide an accurately calibrated attenuator. What good is such a generator for use with an fm receiver claiming a sensitivity of 2 microvolts if the generator "leaks" a couple of hundred microvolts right out of its metal cabinet? To provide proper shielding and a calibrated attenuator costs a great deal of money and requires precision machining and assembly of parts.

Figs. 9-7 and 9-8 are typical response curves photographed directly from the face of an oscilloscope. You can readily see how much information can be gained about the state of alignment of the sets involved just from looking at the photos.

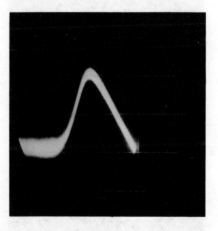

Fig. 9-7. Typical response curve obtained during i-f sweep alignment.

Final alignment of either the ratio-detector or the discriminator is even more easily accomplished using the visual method, for, as can be seen in Fig. 9-9, the "S" curve discussed earlier (in Chapter 6) is beautifully displayed, revealing such data as linear portion (over how many kHz the slope is uniform, so that recovered audio is distortion free), distance (in kHz) from peak to peak, etc. While zero-centering

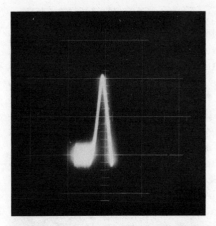

Fig. 9-8. A response curve indicating narrow bandwidth (scope settings are the same as for Fig. 9-7).

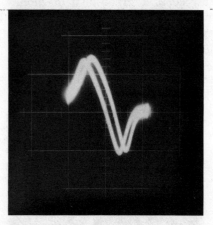

Fig. 9-9. Classical "S" curve obtained at output of fm detector during sweep alignment.

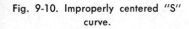

Fig. 9-10. Improperly centered "S" curve.

of the detector response is effectively done using the meter method, Figs. 9-10 and 9-11 show exactly what happens to the response when the secondary of the detector is *not* adjusted

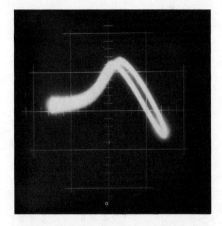

Fig. 9-11. Another example of an off-centered "S" curve.

for proper zero-center. A manufacturer presenting alignment instructions for the visual method might tabulate these instructions as shown in Table 9-2.

RF OR FRONT END ALIGNMENT

Alignment of the rf sections of an fm tuner or receiver is surprisingly similar to the methods used for am radio alignment. Most rf tuned circuits are single-tuned (or single-peaked) which requires that they simply be tuned for maximum output. This make rf adjustment actually simpler in many respects than i-f adjustment. Rf alignment should never be attempted unless the i-f system is known to be in perfect alignment. In addition, if an afc circuit is present in the tuner or receiver, it should be defeated or deactivated before rf alignment is undertaken.

In most cases, alignment of the rf section will include making certain that the receiver, after alignment, meets its published specifications, particularly with regard to quieting sensitivity, or IHF "least usable sensitivity." For this reason, it now becomes imperative that the exact number of microvolts reaching the antenna terminals of the receiver under test be known. With today's ultrasensitive tuners and receivers, this means that the rf generator used must be capable of attenuation

Table 9-2. Oscilloscope Alignment

FM IF ALIGNMENT USING FM SIGNAL GENERATOR - SELECTOR IN FM POSITION

High side thru .01mfd to pin 2 (grid) of FM Mixer, low side to chassis. Use minimum marker signal. Use 60ᵥ frequency modulated signal with 450KC sweep. Use 60ᵥ sawtooth voltage in scope for horizontal deflection.

	GENERATOR FREQUENCY	DIAL SETTING	INDICATOR	ADJUST	REMARKS
4.	10.7MC (450KC Swp.)	Point of non-interference	Vert. amp. of scope to point Ⓑ, low side to ground.	A11, A12 A13, A14 A15, A16 A17	Disconnect stabilizing capacitor C4. Adjust for maximum gain and symmetry of response similar to Fig. 1 with marker as shown. Reconnect C4.
5.	"	"	Vert. amp. to point Ⓒ, low side to ground.	A18	Adjust A18 (secondary) to place marker at center of "S" curve similar to Fig. 2. Adjust A11 (primary) for maximum amplitude and straightness of line.

10.7MC

FIG. 2

FM RF ALIGNMENT - SELECTOR IN FM POSITION

Connect generator across antenna terminals with 120Ω carbon resistors in series with each lead.

	GENERATOR FREQUENCY	DIAL SETTING	INDICATOR	ADJUST	REMARKS
6.	105MC (unmod.)	105MC	DC probe of VTVM to point Ⓑ, common to chassis.	A19, A20 A21	Adjust for maximum.
7.	90MC	90MC	"	L5, L4 L3	Adjust for maximum deflection by expanding or compressing coil turns.

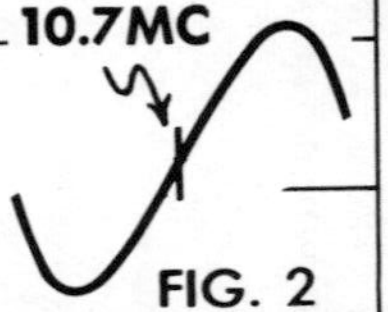

down to a fraction of a microvolt. Furthermore, when the generator output is reduced to its minimum, there must be no leakage or radiation of rf from the transmission cable, the generator metal housing, or even the ac power cord. These shielding requirements are part of what makes good fm generators so expensive.

Manufacturers involved in the design and production of fm receiving equipment often test their products in a magnetically and electrostatically shielded room, often called a "screen room," since tightly woven copper screening is usually used to cover walls, ceiling, and floor, as well as any doorways leading into the room. The use of such a shielded room prevents broadcast signals from nearby stations from interfering with the alignment and test process. The IHF standard for tuner measurement (and alignment) requires that tests be made at three frequencies: 90 MHz, 98 MHz and 106 MHz. Since there may well be stations within 100 kHz of all of these frequencies, it is important to block out reception of these stations and deal only with the rf produced by the signal generator.

As mentioned previously, the co-axial cable should connect rf energy to the antenna terminals by means of a matching network. Most generators have an internal output impedance of 50 ohms, while most fm tuners have input impedances of either 75 ohms or, more popularly, 300 ohms. In the case of a balanced 300-ohm system (the most popular type), the network shown in Fig. 9-12 should be used to provide a proper match between generator and receiver or tuner. Since a voltage drop will take place across the series resistors, however, the actual number of microvolts reaching the tuner or receiver antenna terminals will be *half* the number of microvolts read on the calibrated dial of the generator.

Test points for connecting a VTVM or an oscilloscope are the same as those used for i-f alignment, since the i-f system, having been previously aligned, is now being used as a fixed amplifier. If using a meter as the indicator, the steps to be followed are these:

1. Tune the tuner dial to 106 MHz and set the fm signal generator to the same frequency.

2. Adjust the oscillator section trimmer capacitor for a peak indication, rocking the trimmer adjustment back and forth a couple of times to make sure absolute peak has been

achieved. Always work with the *least* amount of rf signal consistent with on-scale meter readings, using the lowest available scale of the VTVM.

3. Adjust trimmers of all rf sections of the variable capacitor for a peak reading. The number of trimmers will depend upon the number of tuned sections there are in the rf section of the set under test.

4. Repeat all adjustments, at a lower signal level, if possible. In many circuits, adjustment of one trimmer may affect the adjustment of others, and so the final adjustment points should be "zeroed in" by repeated adjustments—including even the local oscillator trimmer.

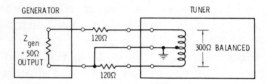

Fig. 9-12. Matching network required for connecting 50-ohm generator to 300-ohm balanced antenna input. Dotted connection may be omitted with practically no increase in mismatch.

5. Set the tuner dial to 90 MHz and set the generator frequency to this frequency as well. Adjust the oscillator coil for a peak reading. Note, that in many sets, the oscillator coil as well as all other rf coils consist simply of a few turns of wire wound in open air and having no tuning slug or supporting coil form. Such coils are adjusted by carefully compressing or expanding the turns a small amount, depending upon which action results in a higher reading on the meter. More sophisticated front ends will have rf coils wound on ceramic or other forms and may even provide tuning slugs, much like i-f transformers and coils.

6. Adjust such other rf coils as may be present (again, depending upon the number of tuned rf stages) for a maximum indication on the meter. Repeat steps 5 and 6 as many times as needed, always reducing signal strength to minimum required, until an absolute maximum reading is obtained.

7. If considerable adjustment of coils was required, it is necessary to return to a frequency of 106 MHz and touch up all the trimmers once more, repeating all of the above steps

until no further increase in reading is attainable at either 90 MHz or 106 MHz.

VISUAL RF ALIGNMENT

Sweep alignment of the rf section of an fm tuner or receiver is quite similar to the procedures already outlined for i-f alignment. We have found that it is best to observe the detector "S" curve for this procedure, rather than the limiter or agc voltage, since by doing so it is possible to maintain the best overall output response and linearity. This procedure, too, has advantages over the static meter method, since it is possible, using just a meter as an indicator, to inadvertently tune the rf stages in such a manner as to reduce usable bandwidth. In observing the output "S" curve, on the other hand, the objective is to increase overall gain of the system without distorting or narrowing the "S" curve previously achieved during i-f alignment.

The foregoing alignment procedures are necessarily general, since no two tuners or receivers are alike. Fortunately, just about every reputable manufacturer marketing high-fidelity tuners and receivers takes the trouble to prepare a detailed service manual. While individual procedures outlined in your service manual may differ somewhat from the general methods outlined here, the objectives are always the same—to bring performance up to "mint" condition. A bit of time spent studying specific suggestions of manufacturers will enable you to relate them to the discussion here.

We stressed, at the outset, the need for good test equipment in servicing fm equipment, and it bears repeating. Experience in dealing with these high-frequency, critical circuits is also a vital ingredient for successful servicing and alignment of your own system or someone else's. It is NOT the kind of equipment one should attack with just a screwdriver and a pair of pliers. Without proper equipment and experience, you would be much better off letting your local serviceman align your fm set—preferably about once a year for tube sets, and perhaps every two years for newer, solid-state equipment.

Index